Skills Practice
Blackline Masters

Level 4
Book 2

SRA

Columbus, OH

SRAonline.com

 SRA

Send all inquiries to this address:
SRA/McGraw-Hill
4400 Easton Commons
Columbus, OH 43219-6188

ISBN: 978-0-07-610509-0
MHID: 0-07-610509-1

3 4 5 6 7 8 9 QPD 13 12 11 10 09 08

Unit 4 Science Fair

Unit 5 America on the Move

Unit 6 Dollars and Sense

Name _____ Date _____

Root Plus Suffix *-ic, -ly, -ist, -er*

Focus

A **suffix** is an addition to the end of a word. Example: call*ing*

A **root word** is a word to which a suffix can be added. Example: <u>call</u>ing

Adding the **suffix *-ly*** to the end of words changes adjectives to adverbs, which describe the way something occurs. Example: *happily*

The **suffix *-ly*** also changes root words that are nouns into adjectives. Example: *fatherly*

The **suffix *-ic*** means "having to do with." The root word changes from a noun to an adjective when this suffix is added. Example: *scientific*

The **suffix *-ist*** means "one who practices." In this case, the part of speech of the root word does not change. Example: *scientist*

The **suffix *-er*** changes verbs to nouns. Example: *farmer*

Practice A Add either the suffix *-ic* or *-ly* to make a new word.

1. **sister** _____

2. **hieroglyph** _____

3. **magnet** _____

4. **quick** _____

5. **complete** _____

6. **prophet** _____

Practice B Add either the suffix *-ist* or *-er* to make a new word. Remember that when adding the suffix *-ist*, the final letter of the root word is often dropped.

7. dream _____

8. biology _____

9. pharmacy _____

10. paint _____

11. sell _____

12. piano _____

13. train _____

14. play _____

Apply Add a suffix to each word (*-ic, -ly, -ist, or -er*) to make it the part of speech written in parentheses. Then write each new word in a sentence.

15. teach (noun) _____

_____

16. sudden (adverb) _____

_____

17. geology (noun) _____

_____

18. volcano (adjective) _____

_____

Name _____ Date _____

Selection Vocabulary

Focus

crabbier (kra' • bē • ûr) *adj.* form of **crabby:** cross; in a bad mood (page 355)

local (lō' • kəl) *adj.* nearby (page 356)

observations (ob' • sûr • vā' • shənz) *n.* plural of **observation:** an act of noticing something (page 358)

examine (ik • za' • mən) *v.* to look closely (page 359)

certain (sûr' • tən) *adj.* sure (page 363)

react (rē • akt') *v.* to act because something has happened (page 363)

results (ri • zults') *n.* plural of **result:** what you find out when you do an experiment (page 362)

anxious (angk' • shəs) *adj.* eager (page 366)

Practice Write the vocabulary word that best matches the underlined word or phrase in the sentences below.

1. You might want to <u>inspect</u> the carton of eggs to see if any are cracked. _____

2. Trevor didn't <u>respond</u> to his father's news very well.

   _____

3. Ashley was <u>concerned</u> about the trip.

   _____

4. We must remember to record the <u>findings</u> of our science experiment. _____

5. Molly's little sister is <u>more irritated</u> when she doesn't take an afternoon nap. _____

Apply Fill in the blank with a vocabulary word from this lesson to complete each sentence.

6. I thought you would feel better after a good night's sleep,

   but you seem _____.

7. Are you _____ that the show
   starts at 8:00?

8. If you want the bully to leave you alone, don't

   _____ to his teasing.

9. Kiyama and I didn't get the _____
   we expected when we conducted our survey.

10. Ben ran down to the _____ candy
    store to buy a gift for his grandparents.

11. The doctor will carefully _____
    you during your annual check-up.

12. I like to watch people in the mall and make

    _____ about them.

13. Tanner is _____ to get the race
    started.

Name _____ Date _____

Parts of a Library

Libraries are an important part of your research process. Libraries are full of resources to help you find just about any kind of information you can imagine.

- The reference section contains almanacs, dictionaries, atlases, and encyclopedias.

- Periodicals include magazines and newspapers.

- Fiction books are organized by the author's last name, nonfiction books by subject matter.

- Many libraries provide electronic resources, including periodical databases, reference software, and the Internet.

- Most libraries have card catalogs available electronically, allowing you to search material by title, author, or subject.

Which sections of the library have you used in the past?

_____

_____

Which section of the library is your favorite, and why?

_____

_____

Which section have you found most helpful when doing research? What helpful resources have you found there?

_____

_____

_____

_____

Visit a local library and find the following resources. Write the title of the resource on the line provided.

1. A fiction book by a favorite author

_____

_____

2. A book about science fair projects

_____

_____

3. A magazine about sports

_____

_____

4. An encyclopedia article about dogs

_____

_____

5. A newspaper article about an event in your city or town

_____

_____

Choose a topic related to the scientific method. While at the library, make a list of sources you could use to help you research your topic.

_____

_____

_____

Name _____ **Date** _____

Writing a Summary

**Think** **Audience: Who** will read your summary?

_____

Purpose: What is your reason for writing a summary?

_____

Prewriting **Use this graphic organizer to summarize a story of your choice. Write the main idea and details of the story.**

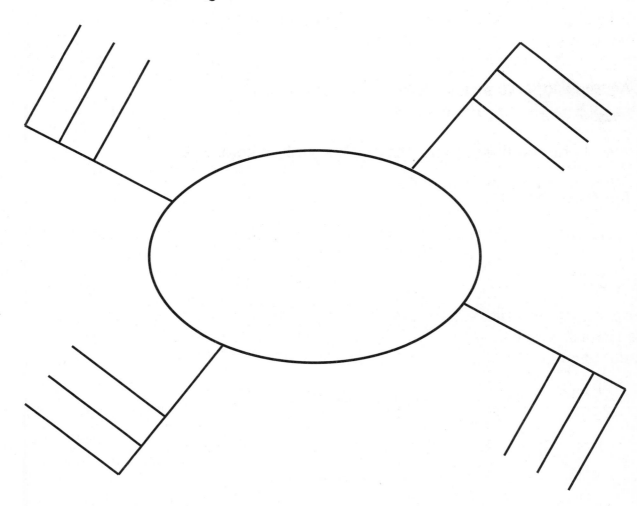

Revising
Use this checklist to revise your summary.

- ☐ Do you write about the main idea of the selection?
- ☐ Do you include only the most important details?
- ☐ Do the other sentences in the paragraph support the main idea?

Editing/Proofreading
Use this checklist to correct mistakes in your summary.

- ☐ Did you check your spelling?
- ☐ Are commas and other punctuation used correctly?
- ☐ Are pronouns used correctly? Do they agree with their antecedents in number and gender?

Publishing
Use this checklist to get ready for publication.

- ☐ Read your summary again to make sure it is complete.
- ☐ Write or type a neat final copy.

Name _____ **Date** _____

Root word plus suffix

Focus
- When suffixes are added to root words, the meaning of the root word changes.
- *–ity* changes an adjective into a noun
- *–al* changes a noun into an adjective
- *–less* means without
- *–or* means a person with _____
- *–ly* means in a _____ way

Practice   **Write the spelling words made from these root words.**

-ity, changes an adjective into a noun

1. local _____   **3.** odd _____

2. humid _____

-less, without

4. price _____   **6.** life _____

5. flavor _____

-or, a person who does something

7. act _____   **9.** inspect _____

8. collect _____

-al, changes a noun into an adjective

10. norm _____   **12.** nation _____

11. critic _____

Copyright © SRA/McGraw-Hill. Permission is granted to reproduce this page for classroom use.

Word List
1. locality
2. oddity
3. humidity
4. finality
5. priceless
6. flavorless
7. needless
8. lifeless
9. actor
10. editor
11. collector
12. inspector
13. normal
14. digital
15. critical
16. national
17. briskly
18. jointly
19. properly
20. vividly

Challenge Words
21. governor
22. certainly
23. entirely

-ly, in a certain way

13. brisk _____ **15.** proper _____

14. joint _____

Apply Write the spelling word you can make with each group of letters.

16. anifiytl _____

17. dvliviy _____

18. loolccetr _____

19. tacro _____

20. clepssrie _____

Add the suffixes –or, -al, -ly, or –ity to write a spelling word. The first one is done for you.

	-or	-al	-ly	-ity
21. inspect	_____	_____	_____	_____
22. nation	_____	_____	_____	_____
23. odd	_____	_____	_____	_____
24. brisk	_____	_____	_____	_____

Challenge

| **25.** certain | _____ | _____ | _____ | _____ |
| **26.** govern | _____ | _____ | _____ | _____ |

Regular Verbs

Focus | **Regular verbs** are verbs that follow a certain pattern when they change tenses.

Laugh is a **regular verb.**

They *laugh.* She *laughed.*

Laugh and *laughed* are forms of the verb *to laugh. Laugh* shows an action currently happening, while *laughed* shows an action in the past.

If the subject of a sentence is singular, most verbs add *-s* or *-es* to create the present tense, but add nothing for plural subjects.

To form the past tense, add *-ed* to the verb.

Practice A | **Change each of these regular verbs to the past tense.**

1. gallop _____

2. play _____

3. follow _____

4. smile _____

Change each of these regular verbs to the present tense.

5. expected _____

6. pulled _____

7. crawled _____

8. rowed _____

Practice B — Circle the correct form of the verb in parentheses.

9. My baby sister (grab/grabs) everything in sight.

10. Kia and Sienna (pick/picked) cherries yesterday morning.

11. Last week, my brother (want/wanted) to go skiing, but now he doesn't.

12. My horses (roll/rolls) on their backs in the grass.

13. We (cheer/cheers) loudly at every football game.

14. Deston likes to (climb/climbed) on the jungle gym.

15. The farmer (ask/asked) his horse if he wanted some hay.

Apply — Rewrite each sentence changing the underlined verbs to the present tense. You may have to change some of the other words in the sentence for it to make sense.

16. My dogs barked all night last night. _____

_____

17. Leeza tied a knot in the rope. _____

_____

18. Alec and Heni reminded the teacher to collect the homework.

_____

_____

_____

Name _____ Date _____

Roots plus prefixes *mis-*, *un-*, *dis-*, and *im-*

Focus The **prefixes mis-, un-, dis-** and **im-** all have a similar meaning: *not*, or *opposite.*

Examples: *mis*fortune, *un*happy, *dis*agree, *im*possible

Practice A Add the correct prefix (*mis-, un-, dis-,* or *im-*) to each word to give it the opposite meaning. You may use a dictionary if needed.

1. judge   _____

2. screw   _____

3. honest   _____

4. conduct   _____

5. infect   _____

6. patient   _____

7. behave   _____

8. perfect   _____

9. pack   _____

10. steady   _____

Practice B

Match each definition below with a word from the word box.

dislike	distrust	impolite	misplace	unnatural	unprepared

11. not have faith in _____

12. not normal _____

13. not be fond of _____

14. put in the wrong spot _____

15. not very nice _____

16. not ready _____

Apply

Write a definition of each word based on the meaning of the prefix and the root word. You may not use the root word in your definition.

17. unskilled _____

18. mispronounce _____

19. disappear _____

20. untidy _____

21. imperfect _____

22. unpopular _____

Name _____ **Date** _____

Selection Vocabulary

Focus

attract (ə • trakt') *v.* to cause something to come closer (page 376)

pure (pyo͞or) *adj.* not mixed with anything (page 376)

rarely (râr' • lē) *adv.* not often (page 376)

force (fors) *n.* the push or pull of something (page 377)

core (kor) *n.* the central, most important, or deepest part of something (page 380)

related (ri • lā' • təd) *adj.* connected (page 382)

current (kûr' • ənt) *n.* the flow of electricity (page 382)

friction (frik' • shən) *n.* the rubbing of one thing against another (page 383)

Practice **Write the word that best fits each clue below.**

1. If two people are in the same family, what do we say

they are? _____

2. What does a flower do to a bee? _____

3. If the water is clean and clear and has no chemicals in it,

what is it? _____

4. What do we call a stream of electricity? _____

5. What is the very middle of the earth is called?

_____

6. What are you measuring when you see how

hard something is pushing something else? _____

Apply   Write the vocabulary word next to the group of words that have a similar meaning.

7. energy; intensity; vigor   _____

8. hardly; infrequently; occasionally   _____

9. moving; rubbing; scraping   _____

10. clean; uncontaminated; untainted   _____

11. associated; connected; aligned   _____

12. stream; flow; line   _____

13. pull; fascinate; bring together   _____

14. inside; middle; depths   _____

Name _____ Date _____

Evaluating Questions for Investigation

When choosing a question to investigate, it is important to select a question that is neither too narrow nor too broad. On the next page, you will learn some strategies for evaluating questions.

Think of a question you have investigated in the past. Write it here.

_____

_____

_____

Was the question too narrow, too broad, or just right? How did you decide this?

_____

_____

_____

The selections in this unit contain many possibilities for investigation. Scan the selections and see how you could further investigate the concept of the scientific method. Write some questions you would like to investigate further.

_____

_____

_____

_____

_____

_____

Evaluation Strategies

- Conduct a search using keywords. If few or no sources are available, the question may be too narrow. If hundreds of sources are available, the question may be too broad.

- Break the question into as many subtopics as you can brainstorm. If you have more than five, your question is probably too broad. If you have only one or two subtopics, then your question is most likely too narrow.

On the bottom of the previous page, you made a list of possible questions. Choose one of them to evaluate.

_____

_____

First, conduct a search on keywords related to your question. You may use the Internet or the library. How many sources did you find? Is this enough/not enough/too many? Why do you think so?

_____

_____

_____

Divide your topic into as many subtopics as you can brainstorm. Write those subtopics here.

_____

_____

_____

Based on your evaluation, is your question too broad, too narrow, or just right? If you need to revise your question, write your new question here.

_____

_____

Name _____ **Date** _____

Organizing Expository Writing

Focus

When you write to give information or to explain something, you must organize the information for your readers. The method of organization usually depends on the type of information you are providing your readers. Three common methods are **compare and contrast, cause and effect,** and **question and answer.**

- You can **compare and contrast** two things to point out how they are alike and how they are different. This method works well for comparing two products, two characters in a book or movie, or two animals, for example.

- You can explore **cause-and-effect relationships.** Historians and scientists often use this method of organization. You might explain events that caused another larger event. You might explain what causes northern lights to appear in the sky.

- You can use a **question-and-answer approach.** Begin by asking a question. Then give the answer by explaining the process or providing background for the readers.

Practice

For each topic, tell whether the writer should organize the writing using compare and contrast, cause and effect, or question and answer.

1. elementary school and middle school

_____

2. the benefits of participating in team athletic activities

_____

3. the impact of watching television after school

_____

Apply

Read each expository paragraph. After each paragraph, tell what method of organization the writer uses—compare and contrast, cause and effect, or question and answer.

4. Have you ever been tricked by nature? Some plants and animals are *supposed* to be tricky. For example, the walking stick looks like a stick so it doesn't get eaten. Chameleons change colors to fool their enemies, and some butterflies' wings have markings that look like owls. The markings scare away birds that might want to eat the butterfly.

_____

5. The team's old So-Hi shoes had great support. They were also sturdy and they lasted the whole season. Everyone on the team was satisfied with them. This season, the team is wearing Troopers. There have been two foot injuries already, and two players have had to replace shoes whose soles were damaged. Team members agree that So-Hi shoes seem to be of better quality than Troopers.

_____

What after-school activities take place at your school? Are there athletic teams, art classes, or reading clubs available? Write a paragraph about one or several of these activities. Use compare and contrast, cause and effect, or question and answer to organize your paragraph.

_____

_____

_____

_____

_____

_____

_____

Name _____ **Date** _____

Root words plus prefix

Focus
- When prefixes are added to root words, the meaning of the root word changes.
- *de-* means take away, or do the opposite
- *im-* means not
- *pre-* means before
- *co-* means together, with
- *en-* means to cause to be _____

Practice **Write the spelling words made from these root words.**

de-, to take away or do the opposite

1. claw _____ **2.** rail _____

im-, not

3. polite _____ **5.** perfect _____

4. mobile _____

pre, before

6. view _____ **8.** school _____

7. heat _____

en-, to cause to be _____

9. force _____ **11.** rich _____

10. close _____

Word List
1. deflate
2. demerit
3. declaw
4. derail
5. impure
6. immobile
7. imperfect
8. impolite
9. prefix
10. preview
11. preheat
12. preschool
13. costar
14. copilot
15. cohost
16. copay
17. enlarge
18. enclose
19. enrich
20. enforce

Challenge Words
21. dehydrate
22. immature
23. cooperate

Spelling (continued)

co-, together, with

12. host _____   **14.** pay _____

13. pilot _____

Apply   Write the base word for each word family.

15. larger   largest   enlarge   _____

16. reheat   preheat   heater   _____

17. impure   purer   purest   _____

18. preview   review   viewer   _____

19. enclose   closed   closing   _____

Add the prefixes de-, im-, en-, or co- to write a spelling word. The first one is done for you.

	de-,	im-,	en-,	co-
20. host	_____	_____	_____	_____
21. polite	_____	_____	_____	_____
22. rich	_____	_____	_____	_____
23. rail	_____	_____	_____	_____

Challenge

24. operate _____   _____   _____   _____

25. hydrate _____   _____   _____   _____

Name _____ Date _____

Irregular Verb *To Be*

> **Focus**
>
> The verb *to be* is an **irregular verb. Irregular verbs** do not follow any pattern when they change from present tense to past tense.
>
> | Present | Past |
> |---------|------|
> | **Singular** | |
> | I **am** | I **was** |
> | You **are** | You **were** |
> | He, she, it **is** | He, she, it **was** |
> | **Plural** | |
> | We **are** | We **were** |
> | You **are** | You **were** |
> | They **are** | They **were** |

Practice **Circle the correct form of the verb *to be* in parentheses.**

1. I (am/is) excited about my new puppy!

2. Xavier and Lily (was/were) late for school this morning.

3. The doctor's office (is/are) open on Saturdays now.

4. Your sisters (were/was) wondering where you went!

5. Brownie, my dog, (was/were) my very first pet.

6. The baby bird (was/is) on our porch earlier today.

Apply Read the paragraph. Correct any underlined verbs that are incorrect. Use proofreading marks to correct mistakes.

Melissa's family was moving, and everyone had <u>came</u> to her going-away party. The music was so loud that no one had heard the delivery person when he <u>rang</u> the doorbell with the pizza for the guests. Marcy, Melissa's best friend, <u>come</u> to the party after track practice. Melissa told her that they had <u>sang</u> four songs already and even her little brother Tony had <u>sung</u> "I'm a Little Teapot." Everyone <u>come</u> into the living room to listen to him, because they thought he sounded cute. Melissa's father told her that the telephone had <u>rang</u> while she had been talking to Marcy.

Read the paragraph. Circle the correct verb in parentheses.

When she finished her phone call, Melissa checked to see if everyone had (ate, eaten) the rest of the pizza. Someone told her that her younger sister had (took, taken) the last piece while Melissa had been on the phone. Her parents reminded her that they had (gave, given) Melissa money so that she could order more pizza. Everyone cheered, and Melissa called the pizza place and (given, gave) someone her address again. After that, people (took, taken) a seat in the living room and watched movies until the pizza was delivered. Many of them (ate, eaten) carrots while they waited.

Name _____ Date _____

Spelling Changes with Suffixes

Focus The spelling of a base word sometimes changes when a **suffix** is attached to it.

Sometimes the consonant at the end is doubled before the suffix is added.

Example: **tap, tapped**

Sometimes the final *e* is removed before adding the *-ing* ending.

Example: **excite, exciting**

Sometimes a final *y* is changed to *i* before adding a suffix.

Example: **scary, scariest**

Sometimes the base word doesn't change at all when a suffix is added.

Example: **fast, fastest**

Practice A Add the suffix in parentheses to the bold-faced base word. Make any necessary changes to the root word. Write the new word on the line.

1. smile (-ed) _____

2. big (-er) _____

3. challenge (-ing) _____

4. fly (-es) _____

5. snap (-ed) _____

6. whisper (-ing) _____

7. light (-ing) _____

8. scramble (-ing) _____

Practice B

Circle the word in parentheses that is spelled correctly.

9. The circus is an (exciting/exciteing) place to visit.

10. I (tried/tryed) to call my mom, but the phone was busy.

11. Beth's little brother keeps (shutting/shuting) the lid to the toy box.

12. Cassie (poundded/pounded) on the door until someone answered.

13. What are you (giveing/giving) your dad for his birthday?

14. I think that is the (loveliest/lovelyest) bouquet of flowers I've ever seen.

Apply

Add a suffix to each of the following words and write the new word in a sentence.

15. puzzle _____

_____

16. hot _____

_____

17. connect _____

_____

18. early _____

_____

19. glitter _____

_____

20. drop _____

_____

Name _____ Date _____

Selection Vocabulary

Focus

pursuit (pûr • sōōt) *n.* the act of chasing after (page 392)

drizzly (driz' • ə • lē) *adj.* lightly raining (page 392)

findings (fīn' • dingz) *n.* plural of **finding:** the result of an investigation (page 396)

overwhelm (ō' • vûr • hwelm') *v.* to overpower; to make helpless (page 396)

competitor (kəm • pe' • tə • tûr) *n.* someone selling goods or services in the same market as another person (page 397)

techniques (tek • nēks') *n.* plural of **technique:** a method (page 398)

peered (pērd) *v.* past tense of **peer:** to look closely (page 402)

environment (in • vī' • rən • mənt) *n.* surroundings (page 404)

Practice Circle the correct word that completes each sentence.

1. Aly's kitten darted after the bird in hot _____.
   a. pursuit   **b.** peered   **c.** techniques

2. Recycling aluminum cans helps save the _____.
   a. competitor   **b.** pursuit   **c.** environment

3. Lowell _____ through the hole in the fence to see what his neighbors were doing.
   a. drizzly   **b.** peered   **c.** pursuit

4. If we get a dog, it might _____ our poor little hamsters.
   a. peered   **b.** overwhelm   **c.** competitor

5. It has been _____ outside all day long.
   a. drizzly   **b.** findings   **c.** environment

6. The owner of the store down the street is my father's only _____.
   a. peered   **b.** techniques   **c.** competitor

Apply   Write *T* in the blank if the sentence for the vocabulary word is correct. Write *F* if the sentence is false. For each *F* answer, write the word that fits the definition.

7. *Techniques* are procedures.

_____   _____

8. Your *findings* are your surroundings.

_____   _____

9. *Overwhelm* means "to observe something closely."

_____   _____

10. *Drizzly* means "rain is barely coming down."

_____   _____

11. *Findings* are the answers you come up with when you investigate.

_____   _____

12. Someone who owns the same kind of store you do is your *pursuit*.

_____   _____

13. *Overwhelm* means "running after something."

_____   _____

14. If you *overwhelm* someone, you make him feel like he has no power over you.

_____   _____

Name _____ **Date** _____

Classify and Categorize

Focus

Good readers classify items into categories as they read to help them organize information and understand what they read.

Classifying means arranging people, places, or things into different groups or **categories.** When classifying and categorizing people, ideas, places, or things,

- name the categories, or groups, for similar items.

- list any items that fit the category.

Early American Colonies ←——— *Category*
Massachusetts
Rhode Island
Maryland

Some items can be put in more than one category.

Early American Colonies	**States of the United States**
Massachusetts	Massachusetts
Rhode Island	Rhode Island
Maryland	Maryland

Practice A **Look through "The Case of the Gasping Garbage" and list all the items that fit the categories below.**

1. scientific equipment in Drake Doyle's lab

_____

_____

2. food and drinks Mrs. Doyle made for the scientists

_____

_____

Which of the following does not fit into the same category as the rest? Why doesn't it fit?

skateboard, car, truck, horse, wagon, roller blades, van

_____

Practice B

Name a category that best fits each of the groups of items below. Write the category in the spaces provided.

3. Bananas, grapes, apples, strawberries _____

4. Baseball, basketball, golf, tennis _____

5. Lion tamers, clowns, flying trapeze artists, elephant trainers

_____

6. Richard Nixon, Ulysses S. Grant, Abraham Lincoln, Calvin Coolidge

_____

Apply

Think about the subjects you learn in school, such as social studies and math. Choose your favorite subject and list any items that you might use for that subject, such as a compass for math and maps for geography. Write the subject and the items in the spaces below.

My favorite subject is: _____

Items: _____

Comprehension Skill • *Skills Practice 2*

Name _____ Date _____

Using Indexes to Find Magazine Articles

Most libraries contain two indexes, *The Reader's Guide to Periodical Literature* and *Children's Magazine Guide*, to help you find up-to-date magazine articles. The indexes are published about once a month and are in the reference section of the library.

Features of Periodical Indexes

- The weeks or months when articles were published are on the front cover.

- Articles are arranged alphabetically by headings. After each article title is the following information: author's name, magazine, date of issue, and page numbers. Sometimes no author's name is listed.

- Some subject headings give cross-references to other subject headings in the guide.

Here is a sample of an index entry:

Subject	**TOPIARY:** *see also* Gardening — Cross-reference
Title	Transform Plants into Animals (includes photographs) — Note
Author	E. Blair. *Outdoor Art* Aug '04 p14-20 — Page
Magazine	Date

SUBJECT of the magazine article. Subjects are listed in alphabetical order.

CROSS-REFERENCES indicate that more information on this subject can be found in another place in the index.

TITLE of the magazine article. Titles are listed in alphabetical order.

NOTES are added by the editor to give more information about the magazine article.

MAGAZINE in which the article appears.

DATE the magazine was published (month and year).

Page NUMBERS where the articles will be found in the magazine.

Choose a subject related to this unit. Find three articles on this subject using *The Reader's Guide to Periodical Literature* and *Children's Magazine Guide.* For each article, write the name of the magazine, the title of the article, the author of the article, and the date.

Your Subject _____

Article 1

Magazine _____

Title of Article _____

Author _____

Date of Publication _____

Article 2

Magazine _____

Title of Article _____

Author _____

Date of Publication _____

Article 3

Magazine _____

Title of Article _____

Author _____

Date of Publication _____

Name _____ Date _____

Writing a Summary from Two Sources

Think

Audience: Who will read your summary?

_____

Purpose: What is your reason for writing a summary?

_____

Prewriting

Use this graphic organizer to summarize your two sources. Write the main idea and details of each source.

Main Idea

Main Idea

_____   _____

_____   _____

_____   _____

_____   _____

_____   _____

_____   _____

_____   _____

_____   _____

Revising
Use this checklist to revise your summary.

☐ Do you focus on the main idea of the source?

☐ Do you include only the most important details?

☐ Do the rest of your sentences support the main idea?

Editing/Proofreading
Use this checklist to correct mistakes in your summary.

☐ Did you check your spelling?

☐ Are all commas placed correctly?

☐ Did you write in complete sentences?

Publishing
Use this checklist to get ready for publication.

☐ Read your summary again to make sure it is complete.

☐ Write or type a neat final copy.

Name _____ Date _____

Spelling changes with affixes

Focus

- Sometimes the spelling of a base word changes when you add a suffix. Many words change in predictable ways. Some changes are less predictable.

- If a word ends in *e* and the ending begins with a vowel, the *e* is dropped.

Practice A

Write the spelling words that end in *–or* or *-ous*.

1. _____   4. _____

2. _____   5. _____

3. _____   6. _____

Challenge

7. _____   8. _____

Write the spelling words that end in *-ity*.

9. _____   11. _____

10. _____   12. _____

Challenge

13. _____

Write the spelling words that end in *–ment*.

14. _____   15. _____

Word List

1. drizzly
2. crumbly
3. sensibly
4. terribly
5. activity
6. rarity
7. mobility
8. clarity
9. diversion
10. collision
11. tension
12. intrusion
13. argument
14. supplement
15. elevator
16. juror
17. senator
18. furious
19. nervous
20. cautious

Challenge Words

21. curiosity
22. emperor
23. ambitious

Practice B Look at these examples of spelling words and complete each statement below.

16. diverse   diversion
tense   tension

To add *–ion* to words that end in *se,*

_____

17. collide   collision
intrude   intrusion

To add *–ion* to words that end in *de,*

_____

Apply Write the spelling word that is related to each of these words.

18. crumb _____

19. clear _____

20. jury _____

Challenge

21. empire _____

22. curious _____

Name _____ Date _____

Subject-Verb Agreement

Focus

Subject-verb agreement in a sentence means the verb agrees with the subject in number.

Rule	Example
• The subject of a sentence is either singular or plural. The verb must agree with the subject in number.	• She **works** at the movie theater. We **work** at the movie theater.
• A **compound subject** that uses the conjunction *and* takes a verb that agrees with a plural subject. However, in a compound subject that uses *or*, the verb must agree with the *closest* subject word.	• Justin and Kayla **swim** for the Hillsboro Aquasharks. Their sisters or their brother **cooks** dinner for them every night.
• With a singular subject, add *-s* or *-es* to a regular verb. With a plural subject, do not add *-s* or *-es* to the verb.	• Raul **eats** lunch at the diner. The teenagers **eat** lunch at the diner.
• Irregular verbs have plural forms that are quite different from their singular forms. Do not add *-s* or *-es* to these verbs to make the plural forms.	• Mrs. Kent **has** an appointment. Her daughters **have** a band concert.

Practice A

Read the paragraph. Circle the verb in parentheses that agrees with the subject of each sentence.

How (do, does) people (decide, decides) what to watch on TV? Sometimes, they (take, takes) turns or (flip, flips) a coin. Parents often (tell, tells) their children which programs (is, are) appropriate. Parents (want, wants) to make sure the television programs they choose (is, are) good for kids to watch.

Practice B Read the sentences. Change the underlined verbs to agree with the subject of each sentence. Write the correct words above the underlined words.

1 Fossils <u>is</u> the remains of animals and plants that <u>has</u> died.

2. Fossils <u>forms</u> from objects that <u>is</u> hard.

3. Some fossils <u>looks</u> like dinosaur footprints.

4. A scientist <u>need</u> a microscope when the fossils <u>is</u> very small.

5. A piece of amber <u>trap</u> an insect and <u>create</u> a fossil.

Apply Read the paragraph. Change the underlined verbs to agree with the subject of each sentence. Use proofreading marks. Write the correct words above the incorrect words.

Roxie and Madison <u>takes</u> swimming lessons every week.

They <u>rides</u> their bikes to the community center after school.

Madison <u>enjoy</u> swimming the butterfly, but Roxie <u>hate</u> that

stroke! The girls' parents or their sisters <u>gives</u> them rides

home after practice. Roxie's brother and her dog <u>is</u> scared of

water. They both <u>screams</u> if water <u>touch</u> them. A dog treat or

a pat on the head <u>are</u> a way to quiet the dog. A bowl of cereal

<u>do</u> the trick for Roxie's brother.

Name _____ **Date** _____

Homographs

Focus Do you remember the difference between **homographs** and **homophones?**

Homographs are words that are spelled the same and pronounced differently.

Example: I wiped a **tear** from my eye. Don't **tear** that page, please.

Homophones are spelled differently but pronounced the same.

Example: **Their** house is red. Look over **there!** Today's lesson will focus on **homographs.**

Practice Write two definitions for each homograph.

1. tear _____

_____

2. wind _____

_____

3. dove _____

_____

4. lead _____

_____

Name _____ **Date** _____

Inflectional Endings

> **Focus**
>
> **Inflectional endings** are endings that change the tense of a verb or change a singular noun to a plural noun.
>
> Examples: *-ed, -ing, -s*
>
> Sometimes the consonant at the end of a word is doubled before the suffix is added.
>
> Example: **clip, clipped**
>
> Sometimes the final *e* is removed before adding the *-ing* or *-ed* ending.
>
> Example: **scare, scaring**
>
> Sometimes a final *y* is changed to *i* before adding a suffix.
>
> Example: **party, parties**
>
> Sometimes the base word doesn't change at all when a suffix is added.
>
> Example: **ham, hams**

Practice Add the inflectional ending in parentheses to the bold-faced word. Make any necessary changes. Write the new word on the line.

1. **breathe** (-ing) _____

2. **kite** (-s) _____

3. **library** (-s) _____

4. **carry** (-ed) _____

5. **step** (-ing) _____

6. **snap** (-ed) _____

Name _____ Date _____

Selection Vocabulary

Focus

eclipse (i • klips') *n.* a darkening or hiding of the sun by the moon or of the moon by Earth's shadow (page 424)

inventions (in • vent' • shənz) *n.* plural of **invention:** a thing that is made or thought of for the first time (page 424)

charted (chär' • təd) *v.* past tense of **chart:** to make a map (page 428)

forecasts (for' • casts) *n.* plural of **forecast:** a prediction about what will happen based on evidence (page 428)

charge (chärj) *n.* a load of electricity (page 429)

shocked (shokt) *v.* past tense of **shock:** to jolt by electricity (page 429)

genuine (jen' • yə • wən) *adj.* real; true (page 431)

mast (mast) *n.* a pole that holds sails (page 432)

Practice Circle the word in parentheses that best fits each sentence.

1. How many (eclipse/inventions) do you think Ben Franklin came up with altogether?

2. This battery needs a (mast/charge) if it is going to work.

3. Is that (mast/forecasts) long enough to hold that sail?

4. Mom made me come inside during the storm so I wouldn't get (eclipse/shocked) by lightning.

5. Miriam likes to make (forecasts/inventions) about the results she will get.

6. Vera and I (shocked/charted) the course we wanted our model airplane to take.

7. Is your necklace (charted/genuine) gold?

8. I had never seen an (inventions/eclipse) before today.

Skills Practice 2 • Vocabulary

Apply Match each word on the left to its definition on the right.

9. charted

10. charge

11. shocked

12. genuine

13. mast

14. eclipse

15. forecasts

16. inventions

a. zapped by electricity

b. part of boat the sail is attached to

c. a surge of power

d. when the moon or sun is hidden

e. not fake

f. new devices

g. planned a course

h. estimations of what will happen

Name _____ Date _____

Main Idea and Details

Focus

Writers use a **main idea** and **details** to make their point clear in a paragraph.

- The **main idea** is the most important point the writer makes. The main idea tells what the whole paragraph is about. Often a writer provides the main idea in a clear topic sentence at the beginning or the end of a paragraph.

- **Details** are bits of information in sentences that support the main idea in a paragraph.

Practice A

Find a paragraph in "How Ben Franklin Stole the Lightning" that has a clearly stated main idea. Write the page number and the main idea of the paragraph. Then list two sentences with details the writer gives to support the main idea.

Page _____ Main Idea: _____

_____

_____

Detail: _____

_____

_____

Detail: _____

_____

_____

Practice B

Read the paragraph below. Underline the main idea. Then write two sentences with details that support the main idea.

Today we have vaccines for many different diseases. A vaccine is a special chemical substance that protects us against a certain disease. The substance is made of weak disease germs that cause the body to produce cells to fight off the disease. Recently scientists have developed vaccines for chicken pox and some types of flu.

Detail: _____

_____

Detail: _____

_____

Apply

Write a paragraph about one of your favorite inventions. State your main idea in the first sentence. Then add sentences with details to support the main idea.

_____

_____

_____

_____

_____

_____

_____

Comprehension Skill • *Skills Practice 2*

Name _____ **Date** _____

Organizing Information into Subtopics

One way to organize information is to divide the information into subtopics. You can also use this technique as you are reading to summarize important information.

Choose a topic related to Ben Franklin or the scientific method. Fill in as much information as you can on the chart about your topic.

Topic:		
Subtopics	**Details**	**Details**

Why do you think a chart like this one is such a helpful way to organize information?

_____

Choose another topic from this unit. Find out as much information as you can about the topic and organize it using the chart below

Topic:		
Subtopics	**Details**	**Details**

Name _____ Date _____

Writing a Summary from Two Sources to Compare and Contrast

Think

Audience: Who will read your summary?

_____

Purpose: What is your reason for writing a summary?

_____

Prewriting

Use this Venn diagram to compare and contrast the information you find on your two subjects.

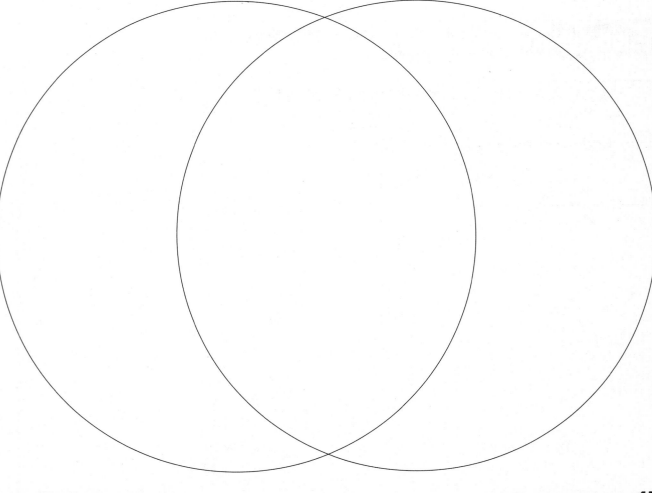

Revising   Use this checklist to revise your summary.

☐ Did you state both comparisons and contrasts?

☐ Is your summary well organized and easy to follow?

☐ Do the sentences in each paragraph support the main idea?

Editing/Proofreading   Use this checklist to correct mistakes in your summary.

☐ Are all words spelled correctly?

☐ Did you use correct punctuation?

☐ Did you capitalize proper nouns?

Publishing   Use this checklist to get ready for publication.

☐ Read your summary again to make sure it is complete.

☐ Write or type a neat final copy.

Name _____   Date _____

Inflectional endings

Focus

- The **inflectional endings** –ed and –ing usually tell when an action *happened,* or *is happening.*

- Sometimes the spelling of a base word changes when you add an inflectional ending. Changes in the base words usually follow familiar patterns.

- If a word ends in e, the e is dropped.

- If a word ends in *consonant-y,* the y becomes *i.*

- If a word ends in *short vowel-consonant,* double the *consonant.*

Practice A **Sort the spelling words into two groups.**

Base word changes spelling

1. _____
2. _____
3. _____
4. _____
5. _____
6. _____
7. _____
8. _____
9. _____
10. _____
11. _____
12. _____
13. _____

Base word stays the same

14. _____
15. _____
16. _____
17. _____
18. _____
19. _____
20. _____

Challenge

21. _____
22. _____
23. _____

Word List

1. charted
2. shocked
3. jerked
4. bowling
5. cried
6. crying
7. married
8. amusing
9. tired
10. jogging
11. strummed
12. grinning
13. webbed
14. feeling
15. pleasing
16. dried
17. controlling
18. equipped
19. willing
20. daring

Challenge Words

21. newfangled
22. occurred
23. increasing

Skills Practice 2 • Spelling

Practice B

Add the inflectional endings –ed and -ing to each base word.

		-ed	-ing
16.	strum	_____	_____
17.	please	_____	_____
18.	bowl	_____	_____
19.	dry	_____	_____
20.	control	_____	_____

Challenge

21.	increase	_____	_____
22.	occur	_____	_____

Circle the misspelled word in each sentence. Write the word correctly on the line.

23. Zack was shoked when he realized he had overslept. _____

24. The handsome prince marryed Cinderella. _____

25. A daring soldier was equiped for battle. _____

Name _____ Date _____

Contractions

> **Focus**
>
> A **contraction** is a shortened form of two words. It is formed by combining two words and leaving out one or more letters. It includes an apostrophe to show where the letter or letters have been left out.
>
> Examples:
> He will = he'll
> Was not = wasn't
> They have = they've

Practice

1. Write four contractions using a verb and the word "not."

_____

_____

2. Write four contractions using a pronoun and the verb "will."

_____

_____

3. Write four contractions using a pronoun and either the verb "is" or "are."

_____

_____

4. Rewrite this sentence so that there are no contractions.
I'll check and see if they're here yet, but I'd say they probably aren't.

_____

_____

Name _____ **Date** _____

Compound Words

Focus

Compound words are made by joining two whole words. The two words do not necessarily keep the same meanings they had as individual words.

In an **open compound,** the words are not combined into one word.

In a **closed compound,** the two words are joined without a hyphen.

Practice   **Solve these compound word riddles.**

mailman stopwatch	greenhouse backyard	eggplant bookworm	firehouse ice box	headache headphone

1. (frozen water) + (square container) = _____

2. (opposite of front) + (lawn) = _____

3. (letters from post office) + (grown-up boy) = _____

4. (color of grass) + (another word for a home) = _____

5. (what a chicken lays) + (something that grows in a garden) =

_____

6. (body part that sits on your neck) + (used to call grandma) =

_____

7. (opposite of go) + (used to tell time) = _____

8. (something you read) + (used to catch fish) = _____

Name _____ Date _____

Selection Vocabulary

Focus

major (mā' • jûr) *adj.* important (page 442)

common (ko' • mən) *adj.* happening often; familiar (page 443)

previous (prē' • vē • əs) *adj.* happening earlier (page 443)

randomly (ran' • dəm • lē) *adv.* by chance (page 443)

questionnaire (kwes' • chə • nâr') *n.* a printed list of questions used by researchers (page 445)

pace (pās) *n.* rate; speed (page 445)

publication (pu' • blə • kā' • shən) *n.* something that is printed or published (page 448)

rejected (ri • jek' • təd) *v.* past tense of **reject:** to turn down (page 448)

Practice Write the vocabulary word next to the group of words that have a similar meaning.

1. casually; pattern-less; haphazardly _____

2. stride; gait; speed _____

3. survey; inquiry; examination _____

4. newspaper; magazine; book _____

5. refused; declined; withheld _____

6. primary; main; key _____

7. before; earlier; past _____

8. same; normal; usual _____

Copyright © SRA/McGraw-Hill. Permission is granted to reproduce this page for classroom use.

Apply Write the word from the word box that matches each definition below.

major	common	previous	randomly
questionnaire	pace	publication	rejected

9. _____ in the past

10. _____ without a pattern

11. _____ putting something into print

12. _____ very significant

13. _____ asking people what they think

14. _____ nothing out of the ordinary

15. _____ said no

16. _____ how fast you are going

Name _____ Date _____

Author's Purpose

Focus
Writers have reasons for presenting a story in a certain way.

The **author's purpose** is the main reason for presenting a story or selection in a certain way. An author's purpose

- can be to *inform*, to *explain*, to *entertain*, or to *persuade.*
- affects things in the story, such as the *details*, *descriptions*, *story events,* and *dialogue.*

An author can have more than one purpose for writing.

Practice A
Look through "How Fast Do You Eat Your Ice Cream?" Identify the author's purpose for writing the story. Find two sentences that show the author's purpose. Write the page number and the sentences on the lines provided. Then, answer the questions below.

Page: _____ Sentence: _____

_____

Page: _____ Sentence: _____

_____

What is the author's purpose for writing the story?

_____

_____

How successful was the author in achieving her purpose? Explain your answer.

_____

_____

Practice B   Writers can have more than one purpose for writing a selection. What other purpose did the author of "How Fast Do You Eat Your Ice Cream?" have?

_____

Find two sentences that show the author's secondary purpose. Write the page number and the sentences on the lines provided. Then answer the questions below.

Page: _____   Sentence: _____

_____

Page: _____   Sentence: _____

_____

When authors _inform_, they give specific facts. When they _explain_, they tell how or why.

Apply   Write a paragraph about a scientific topic of your choice. In your paragraph, include either details that inform or details that explain.

_____

_____

_____

_____

_____

_____

_____

_____

Name _____ Date _____

Asking Questions to Find Information

"How Fast Do You Eat Your Ice Cream?" includes topics such as ice cream headaches and testing hypotheses. Based on the story, fill in the chart with questions about four topics you would like to investigate. Write one question for each topic. Then find answers to your questions either by rereading the selection or by investigating the information in another source.

Questions About a Topic	Information I Found
1.	
2.	

Questions About a Topic	Information I Found	
3.		
4.		

Name _____ Date _____

Ordering Details in Descriptive Writing

Focus

When you are describing a place, thing, or even a person, you can write your description using top-to-bottom or left-to-right organization to help the reader see what you are describing.

Rule

• Place and location words help readers see where things are in your descriptions.

• For things that are mostly vertical, such as a person standing, describe them using top-to-bottom (or bottom-to-top) organization.

• For things that are mostly horizontal, such as an automobile or things in a room, describe them using left-to-right (or right-to-left) organization.

Example

• Here are some examples of place and location words.

above   below   beside   on

across   under   over   near

• Jared has black curly hair. His eyes are dark brown, and he has a cute button nose.

• On the left side of the room is my desk with my computer on it. Next to the desk stands a black floor lamp. On the right side of my room is a chair I throw all my clothes on.

Practice Underline the place and location words and write which type of organization is used in the paragraph.

I rearranged the shelves so my one-year-old brother couldn't get into trouble. I put breakable things on the top shelf and unbreakable things on the middle shelf. I put the things he could play with on the bottom shelf.

What type of organization is used in this paragraph?

Explaining a Scientific Process

Think

Audience: Who will read your scientific process?

_____

Purpose: What is your reason for writing a scientific process?

_____

Revising **Use this checklist to revise your explanation.**

☐ Is each step clearly written?

☐ Have you left out any important steps or information?

☐ Did you include words that show the order of the steps?

☐ Did you explain why this process is important to readers?

Editing/Proofreading **Use this checklist to correct mistakes in your explanation.**

☐ Did you check your spelling, even if you used a computer spell-checker?

☐ Do all your sentences have the correct end punctuation?

☐ Do you use commas correctly in compound and complex sentences?

Publishing **Use this checklist to get ready for publication.**

☐ Read your process again to make sure it is complete.

☐ Include a diagram or other illustration to help readers understand the process.

☐ Write or type a neat final copy.

Name _____ **Date** _____

Compound words

Focus Compound words are words made by combining two or more smaller words.

Practice Break each compound word into two smaller words.

1. _____ _____   11. _____ _____

2. _____ _____   12. _____ _____

3. _____ _____   13. _____ _____

4. _____ _____   14. _____ _____

5. _____ _____   15. _____ _____

6. _____ _____   16. _____ _____

7. _____ _____   17. _____ _____

8. _____ _____   18. _____ _____

9. _____ _____   19. _____ _____

10. _____ _____   20. _____ _____

Challenge

21. _____ _____

22. _____ _____

23. _____ _____

Word List

1. everyone
2. sideways
3. laptop
4. playground
5. bathtub
6. swimsuit
7. mailbox
8. goldfish
9. upstairs
10. blueberry
11. heartbeat
12. teaspoon
13. popcorn
14. birthday
15. fireplace
16. keyboard
17. yearbook
18. rainbow
19. wheelchair
20. townhouse

Challenge Words

21. nighttime
22. handkerchief
23. quarterback

Use the two smaller words that make up the compound word to write the meaning of the compound word. You may use a dictionary to find the meanings of words you do not know. The first one is done for you.

24. fireplace _____

25. wheelchair _____

26. mailbox _____

27. heartbeat _____

28. playground _____

29. goldfish _____

30. birthday _____

Challenge

31. nighttime _____

32. handkerchief _____

Underline the correct spelling of each compound word.

33. everone   everywon   everyone

34. swimsuit   swimsute   swimmsuit

35. blewberry   bluebery   blueberry

Name _____ **Date** _____

Sentence Tenses

Focus
A **present tense** verb shows an action that is currently happening

She *dances* to her favorite song.

A **past tense** verb shows an action that happened in the past.

She *danced* for hours last night.

Practice **Identify whether each sentence is present tense or past tense.**

1. Rebecca's stomach always <u>grumbles</u> when she is hungry. _____

2. Her brother Mark <u>laughed</u> every time he <u>heard</u> it. _____

3. Eliot <u>wonders</u> how his report card will look. _____

4. Ruth <u>did</u> her homework right before class. _____

5. Steven <u>read</u> all of his comics in one day. _____

6. Francine <u>stands</u> at the front of the line waiting to buy tickets. _____

Apply **Write a sentence using the present tense of to run. Then write sentence using the past tense of to run.**

7. _____

8. _____

Correcting Run-ons and Fragments

Copyright © SRA/McGraw-Hill. Permission is granted to reproduce this page for classroom use.

Focus

Rule

- A group of words that does not express a complete thought is not a sentence, but a **fragment.**

- A sentence with no punctuation or coordinating conjunctions between two or more independent clauses is a **run-on sentence.**

- In a **rambling sentence,** a writer strings together many thoughts. Rambling sentences often have many *ands* in them.

- An **awkward sentence** is a sentence that does not read well.

Example

- Harry's new puppy. Didn't eat her food.

- The puppy has been quiet all day Harry doesn't know if she's sick or not.

- Harry kept his puppy warm and he called the vet and the vet told Harry to give the dog some medicine.

- Harry gave the medicine to the dog and she began to get better, so Harry was very happy about that.

Practice   **Read the sentences. Write either *fragment* or *run-on sentence* in the blank.**

1. From 1941 to 1945, Native Americans. _____

2. These soldiers were members of the Comanche people they helped the United States protect its military secrets during

the war. _____

3. The Germans didn't know anything about the Comanche language hearing more words that were different confused

them even more. _____

Name _____ Date _____

Greek Roots

Focus Because so many English words come from the **Greek,** knowing Greek root words will help you to decode such words.

Here are some common Greek roots and their meanings:

logy = "science of" or "to study"

eco = "environment"

geo = "earth"

graph = "write"

auto = "same" or "self"

photo = "light"

port = "to carry"

path = "feeling"

mim = "to copy or imitate"

Practice Using what you know about Greek roots, write a definition for each of the following words.

1. **ecology** _____

2. **geography** _____

3. **autograph** _____

4. **porter** _____

5. **airport** _____

6. **sympathy** _____

Greek Roots

Focus Here are a few more Greek roots to add to the ones you've already learned:

tech = "art" or "skillful"

nym = "name"

opt = "eye"

ortho = "straight"

cycl = "circle"

tele = "far off" or "distant"

scope = "look at"

Practice **Circle the correct word in parentheses.**

1. A (synonym/orthotic) is a *name* for a word that means the same as another word.

2. An (orthotist/optometrist) is an *eye* doctor.

3. A (telephoto/photographic) camera lens helps you see objects *far away.*

4. When one animal *imitates* another, the behavior is called (synonym/mimicry).

Apply **Write a sentence using each of the following words. Check a dictionary if you are unsure of their meanings.**

5. optic nerve _____

_____

6. sympathize _____

_____

Word Structure • *Skills Practice 2*

Name _____ Date _____

Selection Vocabulary

Focus

buzzing (bu' • zing) *v.* form of **buzz:** to be very active (page 468)

ceremony (sâr' • ə • mō • ə) *n.* a formal event, usually with speech making (page 468)

transcontinental (trants' • kon' • tə • nen' • təl) *adj.* stretching from coast to coast (page 468)

laborers (lā' • bûr • ûrz) *n.* plural form of **laborer:** a worker (page 469)

assistance (ə • sis' • tənts) *n.* help (page 469)

hastily (hā' • stə • lē) *adv.* in a hurry (page 470)

locomotives (lō' • kə • mō' • tivz) *n.* plural of **locomotive:** a train engine (page 470)

thrive (thrīv) *v.* to be successful (page 471)

Practice **Circle the word in parentheses that best fits each sentence.**

1. The (laborers/locomotives) are my favorite part of the trains.

2. Aunt Suzie (hastily/thrive) grabbed her purse and ran out the door.

3. On Friday afternoons, our classroom is always (buzzing/ceremony) with activity.

4. If anyone needs (buzzing/assistance), Mrs. Green will help.

5. Elsie's grandfather is being honored at a special (ceremony/locomotives) this evening.

6. Brice hopes his family's new apple tree will (assistance/thrive) in their backyard.

Selection Vocabulary

Apply — Match each word on the left to its definition on the right.

7. laborers		**a.**	quickly; in a rush
8. transcontinental		**b.**	aid
9. hastily		**c.**	to be very active
10. ceremony		**d.**	a ritual act performed in a certain manner
11. buzzing		**e.**	a vehicle used to move railroad cars
12. assistance		**f.**	prosper
13. locomotives		**g.**	people who are paid to do a job
14. thrive		**h.**	from one end of a country to another

Name _____ Date _____

Fact and Opinion

Focus Writers use **facts and opinions** to support ideas in their writing.

A **fact** is a statement that can be proven true.

An **opinion** is what someone feels or believes is true.

Opinions cannot be proven true or false.

Practice A Look at each statement about "The Golden Spike." In the space next to each statement, write *fact* if the statement is a fact. Write *opinion* if it is an opinion.

1. The Central Pacific line had started in San Francisco and built east.

_____

2. Thomas Durant was the vice president of the Union Pacific.

_____

3. The Irish workers worked harder than the Chinese workers.

_____

4. Leland Stanford missed his first attempt at driving in the golden spike.

_____

5. Stanford wasn't very good at using a hammer. _____

6. The ceremony took place in the town of Promontory, Utah.

_____

Fact and Opinion

Practice B — Add a fact or opinion to each sentence below. Use the clues in parentheses.

7. (opinion) All cats like to _____.

8. (fact) All books have _____.

9. (fact) Some birds are _____.

10. (opinion) All children are _____.

Apply — The Golden Spike ceremony was a celebration. Finishing a long hard job was something to celebrate. Think of a time you celebrated something. Write two facts and two opinions about your celebration.

11. (fact) _____

_____

12. (fact) _____

_____

13. (opinion) _____

_____

14. (opinion) _____

_____

Name _____ Date _____

Making a List

Think

Audience: Who will read your list?

_____

Purpose: What is your reason for writing a list?

_____

_____

Prewriting

Use this graphic organizer to organize your list. Remember to arrange your items in order of importance.

Title: "Equipment needed for Promontory Ceremony"

1. _____
2. _____
3. _____
4. _____
5. _____
6. _____
7. _____
8. _____
9. _____
10. _____

Revising
Use this checklist to revise your list.

☐ Is your most important item listed first, and so on?

☐ Does each item meet your original stated purpose?

☐ Would your list make complete sense to someone reading it?

Editing/Proofreading
Use this checklist to correct mistakes in your list.

☐ Did you check your spelling?

☐ Are commas and other punctuation used correctly?

☐ Did you capitalize proper nouns?

Publishing
Use this checklist to get ready for publication.

☐ Read your list again to make sure it is complete.

☐ Write or type a neat final copy. Add illustrations as necessary to clarify an item or items.

Name _____ **Date** _____

Greek Roots

Focus Many English words contain Greek roots. If you know the spellings and meanings of common Greek roots, you can figure out how to spell and define words that contain the roots.

The Greek root **arch** means "chief or first."

The Greek root **bio** means "life."

The Greek root **chron** means "time."

The Greek root **erg** means "work."

The Greek root **hydr** means "water."

The Greek root **therm** means "heat."

The Greek root **typ** means "print or model."

Word List

1. chronic
2. chronology
3. chronicle
4. biome
5. biology
6. bionic
7. biography
8. energy
9. energetic
10. hydrate
11. hydrogen
12. hydrant
13. thermal
14. thermometer
15. thermostat
16. monarch
17. architect
18. type
19. typical
20. prototype

Challenge Words

21. synchronize
22. antibiotic
23. stereotype

Practice Write all the Greek roots you recognize in these spelling words.

1. chronology _____ _____

2. biography _____ _____

3. thermometer _____ _____

Underline the Greek roots you recognize in these words.

4. bionic _____

5. chronic _____

6. energetic _____

7. typical _____

8. hydrant _____

9. thermostat _____

10. monarch _____

Spelling (continued)

Write the spelling word next to its definition.

11. the first model _____

12. a record of events in time _____

13. the study of life _____

14. a device for measuring heat _____

15. the chief designer of a structure _____

16. the ability to do work _____

17. an upright water pipe _____

18. a written account of someone's life _____

19. a community of life _____

20. continuing for a long time _____

Name _____ **Date** _____

Prepositions

Focus

Rule	Example
• A **preposition** is a word that relates a noun, pronoun, or group of words to some other word in the sentence. Prepositions usually indicate relationships of time or place.	• The cookies are **on** the third shelf. They are stacked **above** the crackers.
• The noun or pronoun that follows a preposition in a sentence is called the **object of the preposition.** A preposition must have an object. It can't stand alone.	• The box of spaghetti is **beneath** the **crackers.** (*Crackers* is the object of the preposition *beneath.*) The sauce should be **beside** the **spaghetti.** (*Spaghetti* is the object of the preposition *beside.*)
• A **prepositional phrase** is made up of a preposition, its object, and any words in between.	• The food is **in the cabinet.** The cabinet is **near the window.**

Practice A Read the paragraph. Circle all of the prepositions.

Mongolia is a country on the continent of Asia. It is above China and below Russia. The capital city is near a river. Ulan Bator, the capital city, is one of the largest cities in Mongolia. There are several large cities throughout China and Russia. Have you ever traveled around China and Russia?

Skills Practice 2 • Writing

Prepositions

 **Practice B** Read the paragraph. Circle all of the prepositions. Write the word *object* above the object of the preposition.

Many people travel across North America in cars. The United States is between Canada and Mexico. The Rio Grande River runs along the American border with Mexico, but people can still drive to that country. Several of the Great Lakes are also near our border with Canada, but visitors can drive across them by using a bridge. Families sometimes visit Canada or Mexico during a vacation.

Apply Read the paragraph. Circle all of the prepositions. Draw an *X* through each object of a preposition. Underline each prepositional phrase.

People live in many different areas throughout the United States. Some live with animals on a farm. Others may live in an apartment in a big city. Another group might live near the water, and many children live on quiet streets in small towns. Considering the laws of our country. Americans can choose where they want to live.

Grammar, Usage, and Mechanics • *Skills Practice 2*

Name _____ **Date** _____

Latin Roots

Focus

Many of the English words we use today contain roots that have been borrowed from the Latin language. When you know the meaning of a Latin root, you can begin to figure out the meaning of the English word that contains it.

Here are some common Latin roots and their meanings:

rupt = "break"		*trans* = "across"	
nat = "born"		*struct* = "build"	
cap = "head"		*vis* = "to see"	
sol = "alone"		*mar* = "sea"	

Practice

Based on the meanings of the Latin roots above, write a definition for each of the following words.

1. solitude _____

2. native _____

3. rupture _____

4. captain _____

5. construct _____

6. visible _____

7. marina _____

8. translate _____

Latin Roots

Focus

Here are some more common **Latin roots:**

flect or *flex* = "bend"

dent = "tooth"

cred = "believe"

anim = "life"

form = "shape"

doc = "teach"

aud = "hear"

mov, mob, mot = "move"

Practice

Read the following Latin roots and their meanings. Write another word containing each Latin root beside the one provided.

9. *cred* = "believe"; credible _____

10. *doc* = "teach"; doctrine _____

11. *mot* = "move"; motor _____

12. *aud* = "hear"; auditorium _____

Apply

Write a sentence using each of the following words.

13. immobile _____

_____

14. reflection _____

_____

Name _____ Date _____

Selection Vocabulary

Focus

muscular (mus' • kyə • lûr) *adj.* having well-developed muscles (page 482)

generous (jen' • ər • əs) *adj.* kind and unselfish (page 482)

strain (strān) *v.* to hurt yourself by trying to do too much (page 483)

bulged (buljd) *v.* past tense of **bulge:** to swell out (page 486)

legend (le' • jənd) *n.* a story passed down through the years that is not entirely true (page 489)

versions (vûr' • zhənz) *n.* plural form of **version:** a particular telling of a story (page 489)

Practice Review the vocabulary words and definitions from "John Henry Races the Steam Drill." Write two sentences that each use at least one of the vocabulary words.

1. _____

_____

2. _____

_____

Selection Vocabulary

Apply **Fill in the blank with a vocabulary word from this lesson to complete each sentence.**

1. If you lift weights for six weeks, you'll be more _____.

2. I have heard several _____ of what happened at the party.

3. When she twisted her ankle, it _____ out and began to turn blue.

4. Are you sure that story is completely true, or is it just a _____?

5. Gayle's brother has always been _____ with his possessions.

6. If you run hard for 45 minutes, you might _____ one or more of your muscles.

Drawing Conclusions

Focus Drawing conclusions helps readers get more information from a story.

- **Drawing conclusions** means taking small pieces of information, or details, about a character or story event and using them to make a statement about that character or event.

- The conclusion may not be stated in the text but should be supported by details from the text.

Practice A Look through "John Henry Races the Steam Drill" for details you can use to draw conclusions. Choose and write two different groups of details from the story and the page number. Then, write the conclusion for each.

1. Page: _____ Detail: _____

_____

Detail: _____

_____

Conclusion: _____

2. Page: _____ Detail: _____

_____

Detail: _____

_____

Conclusion: _____

Drawing Conclusions

Practice B   **Read the paragraph, and draw a conclusion.**

For weeks, Marco and Allison talked about getting a pet. Marco wanted a dog for protection, but Allison felt that cats made better companions. Marco argued that a dog was the best choice, because he and Allison worked all day. The dog would bark if someone approached the house, which would help prevent a robbery. Allison felt that a cat would be a better choice, because it could be left home all day more easily than a dog. One day, Allison went shopping. When she returned home, she heard barking in the house.

Conclusion: _____

_____

_____

_____

Apply   **Write the details you used to draw your conclusion.**

Detail: _____

_____

_____

Detail: _____

_____

_____

Observing and Recording Details

Details make explanations clear and more interesting. Details can include sensory information, such as how something looks, tastes, or sounds, that helps form pictures in the reader's mind.

When recording details, do the following:

- Jot down the important words, phrases, and ideas.

- Do not worry about spelling, punctuation, or grammar.

- Answer as many of these questions as possible: *Who? What? When? Where? Why?* and *How?*

Look at the stories in this unit about America on the Move. Think about how certain characters endured hardship, overcame obstacles, and made their mark on the history of our country. Choose a character from any of the stories. Record the details that vividly show that character's struggles or accomplishments.

Character: _____

Details: _____

_____

_____

_____

_____

_____

_____

_____

_____

Observing and Recording Details

Think about your investigation. Write the title of your investigation and five details you plan to include in it.

My investigation title is: _____

_____

1. _____

_____

_____

2. _____

_____

_____

3. _____

_____

_____

4. _____

_____

_____

5. _____

_____

_____

Name _____ **Date** _____

Writing a Tall Tale

Think   **Audience: Who** will read your tall tale?

_____

Purpose: What is your reason for writing a tall tale?

_____

Prewriting   Use the space below to plan your tall tale and practice exaggeration. Remember to use descriptive words.

Character's Name: _____

Character Traits: _____

_____

Setting: _____

What happens first? What happens next? _____

_____

_____

_____

_____

How does the story end? _____

_____

_____

_____

Revising   Use this checklist to revise your tall tale.

- ☐ Do you use exaggeration?
- ☐ Does your plot have a beginning, a middle, and an ending?
- ☐ Do your characters and plot, although exaggerated, still make sense?

Editing/Proofreading   Use this checklist to correct mistakes in your tall tale.

- ☐ Did you check your spelling?
- ☐ Are commas and other punctuation used correctly?
- ☐ Did you use quotation marks correctly?

Publishing   Use this checklist to get ready for publication.

- ☐ Read your tall tale again to make sure it is complete.
- ☐ Write or type a neat final copy. Add illustrations for dramatic effect.

Name _____ **Date** _____

Latin Roots

Focus Many English words contain **Latin roots.** If you know the spellings and meanings of common Latin roots, you can figure out how to spell and define words that contain the roots.

- The Latin root *strain* means "to draw tight"
- The Latin root *legere* means "to read."
- The Latin root *vers* means "turn."
- The Latin root *man* means "hand."
- The Latin root *rupt* means "break."
- The Latin root *sec/seq* means "following."
- The Latin root *prim* means "first or highest."

Practice **Write the spelling words that contain a form of these Latin roots.**

vers

1. _____
2. _____
3. _____

strain

4. _____
5. _____
6. _____

Challenge

13. _____

legere

7. _____
8. _____
9. _____

rupt

10. _____
11. _____
12. _____

14. _____

Word List
1. strain
2. restrain
3. constraint
4. legend
5. legible
6. lecture
7. versions
8. versus
9. adverse
10. manual
11. manage
12. manicure
13. disrupt
14. abrupt
15. erupt
16. secondary
17. sequel
18. sequence
19. prime
20. primate

Challenge Words
21. interrupt
22. rupture

Spelling (continued)

Apply **Meaning Strategy** Write the spelling word next to its definition.

15. to treat the hand _____

16. controlled by hand _____

17. breaking off suddenly _____

18. capable of being read _____

19. to pull or draw tight _____

Family Strategy The Latin roots prim and sec/seq are often associated with numbers and order. List these words as families under their roots.

prime second	secondary primary	primate primitive	sequel sequence

20. _____

21. _____

22. _____

23. _____

24. _____

25. _____

26. _____

27. _____

Spelling • *Skills Practice 2*

Name _____ Date _____

Prepositional Phrases

Focus

Remember: A **preposition** relates a noun, pronoun, or group of words to another word in the sentence. (*in, through, by, with*)

The noun or pronoun that follows a preposition in a sentence is called the **object of a preposition.** (in the *house*, through the *woods*, by *her*, with *me*)

A **prepositional phrase** includes a preposition and its object. (*in the house*)

Sentences that are related can often be combined by putting some of the information into a prepositional phrase.

Example:
Many men built the railroad. John Henry was the hardest working man of them all.

New combined sentence:
Of the men who built the railroad, John Henry was the hardest working of them all.

Practice A   Circle all prepositional phrases in the following sentences.

1. Mom said she could use some help around the house after the game.

2. My friend Stella had never heard of the Washington Redskins until today.

3. Watching football is my favorite pastime in the fall.

4. I enjoy watching the players run into the stadium from the locker room.

5. Why is that player standing behind everyone else?

6. Dad said he will take me to a game for my birthday in December.

Practice B **Combine these pairs of sentences into one sentence using a prepositional phrase.**

7. Mark and Zack are brothers. Zack is the older one.

   _____

8. I've traveled a lot of places. I liked Hawaii the best.

   _____

9. I have read all of E. B. White's books. *Charlotte's Web* is my favorite.

   _____

10. Holli and Monica enjoyed tonight's performance. They liked last night's

    performance even better. _____

    _____

Apply **Rewrite each of the following sentences as two separate sentences.**

11. Of all the subjects in school, math is my favorite. _____

    _____

12. Of the six sports at my school, football has the most participants.

    _____

    _____

Grammar, Usage, and Mechanics • *Skills Practice 2*

Name _____ **Date** _____

Synonyms

Focus

Synonyms are words that have similar meanings.

Examples: *huge* and *enormous*

tiny and *little*

terrible and *awful*

poor and *penniless*

Practice A

Write a synonym for each of the following words.

1. difficult _____

2. sleepy _____

3. friend _____

4. peek _____

5. baby _____

6. grip _____

7. courageous _____

8. social _____

9. tasty _____

10. yell _____

Practice B

Match each word on the left to its synonym on the right.

11. scared

12. beautiful

13. well-behaved

14. kid

15. opportunity

16. talk

17. healthy

18. weave

a. obedient

b. chance

c. pretty

d. speak

e. child

f. braid

g. frightened

h. nutritious

Apply

Write a sentence using a synonym for each of the following words.

19. (talented) _____

_____

20. (calm) _____

_____

Word Structure • *Skills Practice 2*

Name _____ **Date** _____

Selection Vocabulary

Focus

yearning (yûr' • ning) *v.* form of **yearn:** to long; to wish (page 498)

dreaded (dre' • dəd) *v.* past tense of **dread:** to fear (page 500)

translated (trants • lā' • təd) *v.* past tense of **translate:** to change words or thoughts from one language into another (page 500)

mainland (mān' • land') *n.* the main part of a country, as opposed to an island (page 500)

wages (wā' • jəz) *n.* plural form of **wage:** pay received for work (page 506)

strikes (strīks) *n.* plural form of **strike:** a work stoppage as a form of protest (page 506)

Practice   Write *T* in the blank if the sentence for the vocabulary word is correct. Write *F* if the sentence is false. For each *F* answer, write the word that fits the definition.

1. *Yearning* means "was afraid of."

_____ _____

2. If something is *translated,* it is changed into a different language.

_____ _____

3. *Dreaded* means "wishing very hard and long for something."

_____ _____

4. *Wages* are when work is stopped.

_____ _____

Selection Vocabulary

Apply **Circle the correct word that completes each sentence.**

5. Nick _____ the geography test, because he didn't study.

   a. translated   **b.** dreaded   **c.** strikes

6. We took a ferry to the _____.

   a. mainland   **b.** wages   **c.** strikes

7. Sasha _____ her mother's words for the teacher.

   a. dreaded   **b.** translated   **c.** mainland

8. My _____ for my new job are much higher than for my last job.

   a. strikes   **b.** wages   **c.** dreaded

9. I wonder why there have been so many _____ lately at the auto plant.

   a. strikes   **b.** wages   **c.** yearning

10. Hermione has been _____ for a pony since she was little.

   a. translated   **b.** dreaded   **c.** yearning

Name _____ **Date** _____

Sequence

Focus

Writers use signal words to help readers understand sequence. **Sequence** is the order of events in a story.

Writers often use signal words called **time-and-order words** to show

- the passage of time in a story. Words such as *Tuesday, tomorrow,* and *the next day* show time.

- the order in which events take place. Words such as *first, then, so, when,* and *finally* show order.

Practice A Look through "Immigrant Children." Find two sentences with time words and two sentences with order words. Write the sentences and their page numbers in the space below. Underline the time-and-order words in each sentence.

1. Page: _____ Sentence with time words: _____

_____

2. Page: _____ Sentence with time words: _____

_____

3. Page: _____ Sentence with order words: _____

_____

4. Page: _____ Sentence with order words: _____

_____

Practice B

Underline the words that signal time or order in each sentence.

5. We ate lunch at noon.

6. When the snow began, we all put on our hats and gloves and ran outside.

7. First, he inserted the key into the lock.

8. The next day, we all went to the movies.

9. Tomorrow we will do all of our homework and be very happy.

Apply

Write a paragraph about some of the things you did recently. Use time-and-order words to indicate *when* and *in what order* you did each thing.

_____

_____

_____

_____

_____

_____

_____

Name _____ **Date** _____

Interviewing

Interviewing is a way to gather information, an opinion, or a story from one person's point of view. Remember to follow these rules:

- Always ask permission to interview the person. Make sure the person knows how much time you will need for the interview.

- Make up questions that will help you get the information you need. Use questions that begin with *who, what, when, where,* or *why.*

- Write your questions in an organized order, with space after each one for taking notes.

- Speak clearly, and be polite.

- Read over your notes immediately after you leave the interview, while the conversation is still fresh in your mind.

- If you plan to record the interview with a tape recorder or a videotape recorder, ask the person's permission first.

Make a list of people you might like to interview.

_____

Write how interviews might be useful in your investigation.

_____

_____

_____

_____

Interviewing

Write five interview questions.

1. _____

2. _____

3. _____

_____

4. _____

5. _____

_____

Summarize what you learned from the interview.

_____

_____

_____

_____

_____

_____

_____

_____

Name _____ Date _____

Writing a Book Review

Think

Audience: Who will read your book review?

_____

Purpose: What is your reason for writing a book review?

_____

Prewriting

Use the space below to organize your book review.

Title: _____

Author: _____

Summary: _____

_____

_____

_____

_____

_____

My opinion and reason for it: _____

_____

_____

_____

Revising

Use this checklist to revise your description.

☐ Does your review have an introduction, supporting paragraphs, and a conclusion?

☐ Are your paragraphs arranged in an appropriate order?

☐ If you are reviewing a fiction book, were you careful not to give away the ending?

Editing/Proofreading

Use this checklist to correct mistakes in your description.

☐ Make sure the subjects and verbs agree in your sentences.

☐ Check all punctuation to make sure that it is correct.

☐ Make sure that all words are spelled correctly.

Publishing

Use this checklist to get ready for publication.

☐ Write or type a neat final copy.

☐ Give an oral presentation of your book review.

Name _____ **Date** _____

Synonyms

Focus **Synonyms** are words that have the same, or nearly the same, meanings.

Practice Write the spelling words that match each meaning.

felt terror

1. _____

2. _____

line or margin

3. _____

4. _____

5. _____

6. _____

odd or abnormal

7. _____

8. _____

9. _____

Challenge

get or gain

10. _____

11. _____

12. _____

Word List

1. wages
2. salary
3. pay
4. income
5. dreaded
6. feared
7. weird
8. strange
9. unusual
10. color
11. hue
12. shade
13. problem
14. concern
15. trouble
16. crisis
17. border
18. edge
19. boundary
20. limit

Challenge Words

21. claim
22. obtain
23. acquire

Spelling (continued)

Visualization Strategy Look at each group of related words and fill in the missing letters.

13. sal_____ry   pa_____   _____ges   in_____me

14. h_____   co_____   _____ade

15. tr_____ble   con_____   _____isis   prob_____

Meaning Strategy Synonyms may express different shades of meaning. For example, an event described as *weird* sounds like more than just *unusual.* Choose and write the spelling word that you think has the best shade of meaning for each blank in the story.

Tim wanted an increase in his 16. _____, but he 17. _____ asking his boss for a raise. He had solved more than one 18. _____ for the company, and he never made any 19._____. Tim had pushed himself to the 20. _____ and decided he just had to claim a raise.

16. _____

17. _____

18. _____

19. _____

20. _____

Name _____ **Date** _____

Sentence Combining with Appositives

Focus

An **appositive** is a noun that is placed next to another noun to identify it or add information about it.

Reyna, my best friend, is riding to school with me today.

The noun *friend* is an appositive that describes *Reyna.*

An **appositive phrase** is a group of words that includes an appositive and words that describe the appositive. *(my best friend)*

An appositive phrase can combine two sentences into one shorter sentence when one of the sentences provides additional information about something in the first sentence.

Example: Leeza sat talking to Kiyomi. Kiyomi was a fellow immigrant.

Leeza sat talking to Kiyomi, a fellow immigrant.

Practice A Circle the appositive phrase in each sentence. Underline the noun it describes.

1. Papaw, my grandfather, takes me fishing every Saturday in the summer.

2. My cat, Tico, likes to chase bugs.

3. Our bus driver, Ms. Calhoun, is sick today.

4. Pepperoni pizza, my favorite food, is on the menu today.

5. Little Bill, my neighbor, walks his dog early in the morning.

6. I just finished reading *Boggles*, my favorite book, for the fifth time.

Practice B

Change each of the following pairs of sentences into a single sentence, using an appositive or appositive phrase.

7. Rachel and I are going to watch *Little Women*. *Little Women* is my favorite movie.

_____

_____

8. My mom is a librarian. My mom loves books.

_____

_____

Apply

Write a short paragraph about your family. At least three of the sentences in your paragraph must include an appositive phrase.

_____

_____

_____

_____

_____

Name _____ **Date** _____

Antonyms

Focus

Antonyms are words that are opposite in meaning.

Examples:

beautiful and ugly

day and night

dirty and clean

sad and happy

Practice A

If the following word pairs are antonyms, write Yes. If they are _not_ antonyms, write No.

1. fat, plump _____

2. silly, funny _____

3. weak, strong _____

4. neat, messy _____

5. yes, no _____

6. interesting, boring _____

7. smooth, silky _____

8. thin, thick _____

Practice B

Write an antonym for each of the bold-faced words.

9. **late** _____

10. **loose** _____

11. **truthful** _____

12. **win** _____

13. **give** _____

14. **insignificant** _____

15. **outgoing** _____

16. **open** _____

17. **same** _____

18. **harsh** _____

Apply

Tedd and Todd are twins, but they are nothing alike. Everything they do is the opposite of each other. Fill in the blanks with a word of your choice. The first one is done for you.

19. Tedd is smiling. Todd is frowning.

20. Todd is quiet. Tedd is _____.

21. Tedd is brave. Todd is _____.

22. Todd is excited. Tedd is _____.

Word Structure • *Skills Practice 2*

Name _____ Date _____

Selection Vocabulary

Focus

era (âr' • ə) *n.* a period of history, usually several years long (page 519)

demand (di • mand') *n.* the desire for a product or service (page 521)

desperate (des' • pə • rət) *adj.* ready to take large risks with little hope of success (page 521)

borders (bor' • dûrz) *n.* plural form of **border:** artificial line where one country or state ends and another begins (page 532)

ditches (di' • chəz) *n.* plural form of **ditch:** a long, narrow pathway cut in the earth to drain water (page 533)

locals (lö • kəlz) *n.* plural form of **local:** a person who has been living in a place for a long time, unlike newly arrived people (page 535)

Practice Write the vocabulary word next to the group of words that have a similar meaning.

1. need; want; require _____

2. trenches; tunnels; paths _____

3. years; time; age _____

4. edges; margins; dividers _____

5. hopeless; despondent; reckless _____

6. citizens; neighbors; inhabitants _____

Skills Practice 2 • Vocabulary

Selection Vocabulary

Apply   **Write the word that best fits each clue below.**

7. Two people who were alive at the same time in history lived in the same what? _____

8. Countries have special people to defend these. What are they?

_____

9. If you've lived in your town all your life, you're one of the what?

_____

10. The mother bird was willing to do anything to save her babies from predators.

What was she? _____

11. If there aren't enough copies of a video game for everyone who wants to

buy one, we say the game is in high what? _____

12. When driving a car on the road, you should try to stay out of what?

_____

Vocabulary • *Skills Practice 2*

Name _____ **Date** _____

Making Inferences

Focus | Readers make **inferences** about characters and events to understand the total picture in a story.

An **inference** is a statement about a character or event in a story. To make an inference, the reader uses

- information from the story, such as examples, facts, reasons, and descriptions.
- personal experience or knowledge, which is the individual memories and experiences you bring to the story.

Practice A | **Look through "The Dust Bowl." Choose a character or a story event, and make an inference about it. Write the character's name or the story event in the spaces below. Then, write the information from the story, the page number, and personal experience or knowledge, and make an inference.**

Character or story event: _____

Page: _____

Information from the text: _____

_____

_____

Personal experience or knowledge: _____

_____

Inference: _____

_____

Practice B

Read the paragraph, and make an inference. In the spaces below, write the inference and the information and personal experience or knowledge you used to make the inference.

At home, Jeanette takes care of all her family's pets. She also walks two big dogs for Mrs. Yamamoto, her next-door neighbor. In addition to these tasks, Jeanette helps her cousin Lila herd sheep for a farmer. She doesn't yell at the sheep to make them go into the corral the way Lila does. Instead, Jeanette gently pushes them into the corral.

Inference: _____

Information from the paragraph: _____

_____

_____

Personal experience or knowledge: _____

_____

Apply

Write a short paragraph about someone who lived through the Dust Bowl. Use sentences with information that a reader could use to make an inference about that person.

_____

_____

_____

_____

_____

Comprehension Skill • *Skills Practice 2*

Name _____ Date _____

Summarizing and Organizing Information

Summarizing will help you organize information and remember what you have read. When you write a summary, look for the main ideas and important details, and use your own words to tell what happens in the story.

Select a story from Unit 5. Write the title on the line below. Summarize the story by filling in the flow chart. Write the main ideas and important details from the story in your own words.

Title: _____

How does the story begin?
_____
_____

↓

What happens next?
_____
_____

↓

What happens after that?
_____
_____

↓

How does the story end?
_____
_____

Summarizing and Organizing Information

Choose a well-known book or movie, but do not put the title of it in the flow chart. Summarize the story on the flow chart. Then, exchange papers with a partner. Guess the title of the book or movie in your partner's flow chart.

How does the story begin?

_____

_____

↓

What happens next?

_____

_____

↓

What happens after that?

_____

_____

↓

How does the story end?

_____

Can you guess the title? Write it here.

_____

Antonyms

Focus | **Antonyms** are words that have opposite, or nearly opposite, meanings.

Practice | Write an antonym for each of these spelling words.

1. despair _____

2. apart _____

3. boring _____

4. graceful _____

5. mild _____

6. alert _____

7. solid _____

8. request _____

9. lazy _____

10. locals _____

Challenge

11. temporary _____

Word List

1. demand
2. request
3. strangers
4. locals
5. fierce
6. mild
7. active
8. lazy
9. graceful
10. awkward
11. thrilling
12. boring
13. drowsy
14. alert
15. together
16. apart
17. solid
18. hollow
19. hope
20. despair

Challenge Words

21. temporary
22. permanent

Spelling (continued)

Proofreading Strategy Underline the misspelled word in each sentence. Write it correctly on the line.

12. The elephant is not a gracful animal.   _____

13. We used a soild red tablecloth.   _____

14. May I requist a special song?   _____

15. It filled me with despare.   _____

16. You could ask the lokals for directions.   _____

17. The long ride in the car was borring.   _____

Challenge

18. Mother used a permanant marker to label the box. _____

Meaning Strategy Pick your favorite pair of antonyms from the spelling list and write a sentence using both words correctly. Underline the spelling words.

19. _____

20. _____

Name _____ Date _____

Keeping Verb Tenses Consistent

Focus Verb tenses within a sentence or paragraph should be kept consistent. When different verb tenses are used, the sentence sounds awkward.

Incorrect: Jamar and Lenny *ate* their lunch and quickly *drink* their milk.

Correct: Jamar and Lenny *ate* their lunch and quickly *drank* their milk.

Practice If the bold-faced verb in each sentence is correct, write *correct.* If it is incorrect, write the correct tense of the verb on the line provided.

1. I watched out the window for the bus and yelled at Caitlin when I **see** it.

   _____

2. We went to the zoo and **feed** the goats. _____

3. Hunter **rolled** the ball to his dog, and the dog chased it. _____

4. I will try to be at your game to **cheered** for your team. _____

5. She **copied** down her assignment every afternoon and looks over it when she

   gets home. _____

6. My pants **are** getting muddy, but I didn't care. _____

7. Strands of hair slipped out of her ponytail and **fell** in her eyes. _____

8. I celebrated my birthday last week, and my grandma **flies** in from Colorado.

   _____

Varying Sentence Types

Focus

Varying the length and structure of your sentences will make your writing more enjoyable to read.

You can vary your sentences by using sentences of different lengths.

You can also vary the beginnings of your sentences, sometimes using dependent clauses at the beginning, and other times beginning with the subject and ending with a dependent clause.

Practice

The sentences in the following paragraph all sound the same. Rewrite the paragraph, and vary the sentences to add interest.

Kyle and Darnell went to the zoo. They saw many animals. They saw an animal they had never seen before. It was a baby rhino. They liked the rhino. They saw a baby kangaroo too. Darnell liked the kangaroo best. Kyle liked the tigers best. Kyle and Darnell want to go back to the zoo. They want to see the animals again. There are so many animals to see at the zoo.

_____

_____

_____

_____

_____

_____

Grammar, Usage, and Mechanics • *Skills Practice 2*

Name _____ **Date** _____

Contractions

Focus

A **contraction** is a shortened form of two words. It is formed by combining two words and leaving out one or more letters. It includes an apostrophe to show where the letter or letters have been left out.

Examples:

it is = it's

you will = you'll

should not = shouldn't

Practice A   **Write each of the following contractions as two words.**

1. didn't _____

2. we've _____

3. he's _____

4. what's _____

5. won't _____

6. they'd _____

7. wasn't _____

8. we're _____

9. can't _____

10. I'd _____

Contractions

Practice B   **Rewrite the following sentences, changing the underlined words to a contraction.**

11. <u>They have</u> been waiting in line since noon.

_____

12. <u>I am</u> going on vacation to Montana next week.

_____

13. Reid and Kasey <u>have not</u> finished their homework.

_____

14. <u>He will</u> let us know when our pizza is ready.

_____

15. My uncles <u>were not</u> expecting the game to be cancelled.

_____

16. <u>I have</u> already eaten two bananas and <u>should not</u> eat a third.

_____

 **Apply**   **The following contractions have been formed incorrectly. Write the correct spelling of each contraction on the lines provided.**

17. he'ill _____

18. wouldv'e _____

19. willn't _____

20. arn't _____

Name _____ **Date** _____

Selection Vocabulary

Focus

rust (rust) *v.* to have the iron parts turn reddish and scaly, then fall away (page 545)

binoculars (bə • no' • kyə • lûrz) *n.* a tool for seeing far away, made of two telescopes joined together to allow the viewer to use both eyes (page 545)

scarlet (skär' • lət) *adj.* bright red (page 545)

skim (skim) *v.* to move over lightly and swiftly (page 545)

slip (slip) *v.* to put somewhere quickly and secretly (page 546)

ashamed (ə • shəmd') *adj.* feeling shame; being upset or feeling guilty because you have done something wrong (page 449)

Practice Write the vocabulary word next to the group of words that have a similar meaning.

1. drop; fall; slump _____

2. glasses; telescope; optics _____

3. corrode; tarnish; stain _____

4. crimson; red; ruby _____

5. embarrassed; humiliated; mortified _____

6. scan; soar; glide _____

Selection Vocabulary

Apply Fill in the blanks below with the correct vocabulary
word.

1. Celia is afraid she will _____ and fall on the ice.

2. He has to use his _____ to look at the birds in the tree.

3. Mitzi tried to scrub the _____ off of her bike.

4. Paul turned _____ with embarrassment.

5. Steven felt _____ when he was caught telling a lie.

6. She planned to _____ the book again before the test.

Name _____ Date _____

Drawing Conclusions from Information

Good researchers often draw conclusions from sources to bring together the various pieces of information. To **draw a conclusion** means to pair the information given in a source with your own knowledge and reasoning powers to figure out an idea not directly stated in the source.

**Find two sources related to the selection, "Pop's Bridge."
Write some information from each source, and then draw
some conclusions by using the two sources together.**

Source #1 Title: _____

Information: _____

_____

Source #2 Title: _____

Information: _____

_____

Conclusions based on two sources: _____

_____

_____

Choose another topic you might use for your investigation. Select two to four sources to find information about your topic. Write your topic title, your sources, and the information you found from your sources.

Topic: _____

Sources: _____

_____

Write a brief summary of the information here:

_____

_____

_____

_____

_____

Draw conclusions using the information you found about your topic.

_____

_____

_____

Name _____ Date _____

Writing a News Story

Think   **Audience: Who** is the audience for your news story?

_____

Purpose: What is your reason for writing a news story?

_____

_____

Prewriting   Use this graphic organizer to plan the lead, the body, and the close of your news story. Decide how to organize the main points of the story.

1. Write the lead paragraph here. The first sentence should answer the questions *What? When? Where? Who?* The next one or two sentences should answer the question *Why?* ▶

2. This paragraph begins the body. Write the most important details here. ▶

3. Write the next most important details here. ▶

4. Write the least important detail here. ▶

5. Write the closing here. End with a sentence or two that summarizes the story or includes your observations. ▶

Revising

Use this checklist to revise your news story.

☐ Did you tell *who, what, when, where,* and *why?*

☐ Is the lead to your news story interesting?

☐ Did you organize the background information in a logical way?

☐ Have you used specific, interesting words instead of general ones?

Editing/Proofreading

Use this checklist to correct mistakes in your news story.

☐ Are the names of the people in your story spelled correctly?

☐ Are the quotations punctuated correctly?

☐ Did you make sure sentences and proper nouns begin with capital letters?

Publishing

Use this checklist to get ready for publication.

☐ Write or type a neat final copy.

☐ Include a photograph or illustration of your subject if possible.

☐ Share your news story with others. Submit it for publication if you'd like.

Name _____ **Date** _____

Homographs

Focus

• **Homographs** are words that are spelled the same way, but which have different meanings, and may have different origins and pronunciations.

Example: *pro' ceeds* is a noun that refers to money obtained from a business venture *pro ceeds'* is a verb that means to continue after an interruption.

Practice **Write each of these homographs in two columns where they belong. Divide each word into syllables, and use a dictionary to see the different pronunciations.**

Homographs: content, number, permit, refuse, graduate

	noun	verb	adjective
1.	_____	_____	_____
2.	_____	_____	_____
3.	_____	_____	_____
4.	_____	_____	_____

Challenge:

5.	_____	_____	_____

Word List

1. conduct
2. rebel
3. sewer
4. insert
5. reject
6. indent
7. combine
8. suspect
9. desert
10. tower
11. reform
12. permit
13. wind
14. recount
15. number
16. sow
17. contrast
18. moped
19. refuse
20. content

Challenge Words

21. graduate
22. proceeds
23. deliberate

Apply   **Spelling words are used twice in each sentence below. Write the meaning for each word. You may use a dictionary to find two meanings for each homograph.**

I <u>suspect</u> that <u>suspect</u> will be convicted at his trial.

6. _____   **7.** _____

We listened to the <u>wind</u> <u>wind</u> through the trees.

8. _____   **9.** _____

I will <u>desert</u> our troop if we camp in the <u>desert</u>.

10. _____   **11.** _____

The <u>sewer</u> accidentally dropped a needle in the <u>sewer</u>.

12. _____   **13.** _____

Sebastian <u>moped</u> because his <u>moped</u> was stolen.

14. _____   **15.** _____

Name _____ Date _____

Homophones

Copyright © SRA/McGraw-Hill. Permission is granted to reproduce this page for classroom use.

Focus **Homophones** are words that have the same sound but different meanings.

Most people **write** with their **right** hand.

Knowing the meaning of a word is very important when using homophones. If you do not know the meaning of a homophone, you could use the word incorrectly.

Most people **right** with their **write** hand. (wrong)

Practice A **Complete each sentence with the correct homophone.**

sole **soul**

1. A person who helps others has a kind _____.

2. The bottom part of your foot is the _____.

rain **reign**

3. Water that falls from the sky is called _____.

4. The people lived in peace under the _____ of a new king.

stares **stairs**

5. The bright red float got many _____ during the parade.

6. I climbed the _____ slowly.

Practice B — Complete each sentence or phrase with a homophone from the box.

tale	plain	rode	way	fare
tail	road	peace	flower	fair
plane	piece	weigh	flour	

7. Sally wore a _____ dress.

8. The _____ landed smoothly.

9. I had a _____ of cake for dessert.

10. The police department keeps the _____.

11. We use _____ to bake bread.

12. Roses are my favorite type of _____.

13. Our dog wags her _____ when she sees us coming home.

14. The captain of the ship told us a _____ about life at sea.

15. One _____ to paint the ceiling is to stand on a ladder.

16. How much do you _____?

17. The judges were _____ in awarding prizes.

18. The cost of riding on a bus or train is called the _____.

19. I _____ a donkey at the zoo.

20. The _____ was slippery after the ice storm.

Word Structure • *Skills Practice 2*

Name _____ Date _____

Selection Vocabulary

Focus

dawn (dôn) *n.* The time when the sun comes up (page 570)

wove (wōv) Past tense of the verb **weave**: To lace together. (page 570)

pride (prīd) *n.* A feeling of worth and importance. (page 571)

huddled (hu' dəld) Past tense of the verb **huddle**: To wrap oneself tightly. (page 575)

pounded (poun' dəd) Past tense of the verb **pound**: To beat loudly. (page 575)

trembled (trem' bəld) Past tense of the verb **tremble**: To shake. (page 575)

embarrassment (im bâr' ə smənt) *n.* A feeling of shyness or of being ashamed. (page 576)

dared (dârd) Past tense of the verb **dare**: To have the courage to do something. (page 577)

Practice Circle the word in parentheses that best fits each sentence.

1. I could feel the house (tremble/dawn) during the earthquake.

2. A. J. took great (embarrassment/pride) in his fine piece of artwork.

3. Esteban (wove/pounded) the colorful strands of yarn into a braid.

4. The kittens (pounded/huddled) next to each other in the cold barn.

5. Dad (tremble/pounded) on my bedroom door to make sure I was awake.

6. Nan was up at the crack of (wove/dawn) this morning.

7. When Katya fell on the steps, she felt (embarrassment/pride).

8. Vanni (pounded/dared) to pick up the little snake when no one else would.

Copyright © SRA/McGraw-Hill. Permission is granted to reproduce this page for classroom use.

Apply Write *T* in the blank if the sentence for the vocabulary word is correct. Write *F* if the sentence is false. For each *F* answer, write the word that fits the definition.

1. If you *wove* something, you laced it together.

_____ _____

2. If you *tremble,* you shake.

_____ _____

3. *Wove* is when the sun comes up.

_____ _____

4. *Pounded* means "wrapped oneself tightly."

_____ _____

5. A feeling of worth and importance is *embarrassment.*

_____ _____

6. If she *dared* to do something, she had the courage to do it.

_____ _____

7. *Pounded* means "beat loudly."

_____ _____

8. A feeling of shyness or being ashamed is *pride.*

_____ _____

Vocabulary • *Skills Practice 2*

Name _____ Date _____

Exploring Online Media

The Internet has search engines you can use to find information. A search engine is used to search data for specific information by typing in a keyword. The keywords must be specific and concise to help the engine narrow its search.

You can also visit specific Internet sites to find information, such as online encyclopedias, news groups, newspapers, and magazines. Certain sites also provide links to other related sites.

Think of a topic related to "Erandi's Braids" that you would like to investigate. Write your topic on the lines provided. Brainstorm specific keywords you could type into a search engine and write them down as well.

My topic: _____

_____

Keywords: _____

_____

Write the names of some magazines, newspapers, or news stations on the lines below. Search these publications' Web sites to find current information on your topic.

_____

_____

Choose another topic to investigate related to the unit theme Dollars and Sense. Write your topic and possible keywords below. Remember, if you don't find what you're looking for at first, change your keywords a bit or brainstorm some new ones on the same topic.

My topic: _____

_____

Keywords: _____

_____

Write the names of some magazines, newspapers, or news stations on the lines below. Search these publications' Web sites to find current information on your topic.

_____

_____

Write two or three interesting facts you learned about your topic.

_____

_____

_____

_____

Sometimes your investigation will lead you to a narrower or more interesting topic. What other topics might you choose to investigate based on what your online search revealed?

_____

_____

Name _____ Date _____

Writing a Personal Narrative

Think   **Audience: Who** will read your personal narrative?

_____

Purpose: What is your reason for writing a personal narrative?

_____

_____

Prewriting   Use this graphic organizer to plan your personal narrative.

Problem or Conflict:
Actions to Solve Problem or Conflict:
Resolution:

Revising
Use this checklist to revise your personal narrative.

☐ Do you explain the problem or conflict and resolution clearly?

☐ Does each paragraph contain a topic sentence with details that support it?

☐ Do you use sensory details to make your narrative interesting?

Editing/Proofreading
Use this checklist to correct mistakes.

☐ Did you check all names and places for correct spelling?

☐ Did you check all punctuation and capitalization?

☐ Read your narrative aloud and listen for grammar errors.

Publishing
Use this checklist to get ready for publication.

☐ Give your story an interesting title.

☐ Write or type a neat final copy.

Name _____   **Date** _____

Homophones

Word List
1. pride
2. pried
3. rays
4. raise
5. sent
6. cent
7. scent
8. forth
9. fourth
10. air
11. heir
12. guessed
13. guest
14. toad
15. towed
16. toed
17. lessen
18. lesson
19. carat
20. carrot

Challenge Words
21. bazaar
22. bizarre

Focus

- Homophones are words that sound alike. They have different meanings and are spelled in different ways.
- Knowing the meanings of homophones can help us know which spelling to use when words sound alike.

Practice A

Write the spelling word for each meaning below. Then, write a homophone for that spelling word.

1. someone who is invited _____

_____

2. a thin orange vegetable _____

_____

3. someone who inherits _____

_____

4. snooped or meddled _____

_____

5. narrow beams of light _____

_____

Challenge:

6. an open marketplace _____

_____

Practice B Look for seven misspelled homophones in these sentences. Underline the misspelled words and write the words on the lines provided.

Our science teacher taught a lessen about measurement. We guest the weight of different things. He said forth graders should know that a carrot weighs about 200 milligrams. We used pennies on the balance scale, and I removed one sent to rays the other arm and make it equal. Then our teacher let Jeff weigh a small towed from the aquarium!

7. _____

8. _____

9. _____

10. _____

11. _____

12. _____

13. _____

Apply Choose a spelling word to complete each sentence below. Write the word in the blank.

14. We saw a _____ of lions at the zoo.

15. Theresa loved the _____ of her new perfume.

Name _____ **Date** _____

Homophones

> **Focus** Remember, **homophones** are words that sound alike but have different meanings.
>
> Knowing the meaning of a word is very important when using homophones. If you do not know the meaning of a homophone, you could use the word incorrectly.
>
> Read the following sentence:
>
> They're going to throw their shoes over there.
>
> - **They're** is a contraction of *they are.*
> - **Their** is a possessive pronoun and an adjective.
> - **There** is an adverb meaning *at* or *in that place.*
>
> Read the following sentence:
>
> She plans to attend two parties too.
>
> - **To** has many meanings—it is a preposition meaning *in the direction of;* it is part of an infinitive, as in *to drink;* and it shows the recipient of an action, as in *give it **to** me.*
> - **Too** is an adverb meaning *also, in addition, more than enough,* or *very.*
> - **Two** refers to the number *two.*
>
> Read the following sentence:
>
> Look at that bird—it's flying to its home!
>
> - **It's** is a contraction of *it is.*
> - **Its** is a possessive pronoun, as in *its own family.*

Practice

Write a sentence using each of the following words correctly.

1. there _____

2. two _____

Apply

Circle the correct word in parentheses.

3. The cat got (it's/its) fur stuck in the thorn bush.

4. (There/They're) are only three days left until spring break.

5. Do you know if (there/they're) planning to move before school is over?

6. The girl down the street has (too/two) kittens for sale.

7. Laschele came over (too/to) our house last night.

8. Did your parents get (there/their) concert tickets in the mail yet?

9. (It's/Its) such a beautiful day.

10. I'd like a glass of orange juice, (to/too).

11. I think (it's/its) too late to sign up for soccer.

Write a sentence using both of the boldfaced words correctly.

12. there, they're _____

_____

13. too, two _____

14. their, there _____

_____

Name _____ Date _____

Homonyms

> **Focus**
>
> **Homonyms** are words that sound the same and are spelled the same, but have different meanings.
>
> Example: bat
>
> A bat is a small furry animal that flies.
>
> A bat is a stick or club used to hit a baseball.
>
> Homonyms may be the same part of speech, or they may be completely different parts of speech.
>
> Example: play
>
> We play together after school. (verb)
>
> My class performed a play. (noun)

Practice Write two definitions for each of the following homonyms.

1. watch _____

_____

2. fan _____

_____

3. play _____

_____

4. box _____

_____

Apply   Complete each sentence with a word from the box.

fan	play	groom	hit

1. The drama club is producing a _____.

2. We should never _____ each other.

3. I need to _____ my dog before the show.

4. The movie was a big _____.

5. The _____ was late for his wedding.

6. We turn on the _____ when the weather gets warm.

7. We _____ baseball every weekend.

8. I'm a big _____ of action movies.

Write two sentences using the word *fair*. Use a different meaning of the word in each sentence.

1. _____

_____

2. _____

_____

Name _____ Date _____

Selection Vocabulary

Focus

clutched (klucht) Past tense of the verb **clutch:** To hold tightly. (page 588)

longed (longd) Past tense of the verb **long:** To want very much. (page 589)

wobbled (wo' bəld) Past tense of the verb **wobble:** to shake back and forth unsteadily. (page 590)

pruned (pro͞ond) Past tense of the verb **prune:** To trim as a plant. (page 592)

confident (kon' fə dənt) *adj.* Sure of oneself. (page 593)

wearily (wēr' ə lē) *adv.* In a tired way. (page 593)

perched (pûrcht) *v.* Past tense of the verb **perch:** To sit on top of something as a bird does. (page 596)

gleefully (glē' fə lē) *adv.* With great happiness. (page 597)

Practice Write the vocabulary word next to the group of words that have a similar meaning.

1. trimmed; cut; clipped _____

2. certain; self-assured; sure _____

3. exhaustedly; tiredly; faintly _____

4. sat; rested; stayed _____

5. gripped; grabbed; held _____

6. desired; wished; wanted _____

7. wavered; shook; quaked _____

8. happily; merrily; joyfully _____

Apply **Match each word on the left to its definition on the right.**

1. gleefully

2. clutched

3. longed

4. pruned

5. wearily

6. confident

7. perched

8. wobbled

a. desired greatly

b. moved shakily

c. feeling self-assured

d. in a fatigued way

e. cut branches

f. with much joy

g. resting on top of something

h. gripped securely

Name _____ **Date** _____

Author's Point of View

Focus

Every story is told from a specific **point of view.** Writers must decide on the point of view from which a story is told.

All stories are told through a narrator, who is the person who tells the story. The narrator can tell the story from

- the **third-person point of view.** The narrator is an outside observer and uses pronouns such as *he, she,* and *they* when telling the story.

- the **first-person point of view.** The narrator is a character in the story and uses pronouns such as *I, me,* and *my* when telling the story.

Practice

Look through the first two pages of "My Rows and Piles of Coins." Find a sentence that lets you know what point of view the author chose for the story. Write the page number, the sentence, and the point of view. Then answer the question below.

Page: _____

Sentence: _____

_____

Point of view: _____

Why do you think the author chose this point of view?

_____

_____

_____

Practice **Read each paragraph and fill in the point of view.**

1. Mary had never eaten a cucumber in her whole life. When she saw that her plate was full of cucumber slices, she almost gave it back. Then she decided to be brave and eat this new vegetable.

Point of view: _____

2. Damian got a trampoline on his birthday. I got a pair of socks. Everything seems to go right for Damian, but nothing ever goes right for me.

Point of view: _____

3. The garden was full of weeds. It would take hours to pull out all the weeds. Gina promised to take care of the garden, but she was visiting her grandfather. There was no one around to pull the weeds—except me. So I knelt down and got to work.

Point of view: _____

Apply **Rewrite one of the passages above using a different point of view.**

_____

_____

_____

_____

_____

Comprehension Skill • *Skills Practice 2*

Name _____ **Date** _____

Choosing a Question to Investigate

What other questions about dollars and sense would you like to investigate?

_____

_____

_____

Now think about these questions. Where could you begin to find some answers?

_____

Are there people you admire who could help you understand more about dollars and sense? Who are they? How could they help?

_____

Think of two or three people you know personally and admire for their expertise with money. Write their names here.

_____

_____

Choose one of these people to interview. I choose

_____

Before you conduct your interview, make a list of five questions you would like to ask this person. Write them here.

_____

_____

_____

_____

Write your interviewee's answers here.

_____

_____

_____

_____

How will these answers help you with your investigation?

_____

_____

_____

Inquiry • *Skills Practice 2*

Name _____ **Date** _____

Homonyms/Multiple-Meaning Words

Focus **Homonyms**/multiple meaning words are words that are spelled and pronounced the same way. They have different meanings and may be different parts of speech.

Practice A Say each spelling word to yourself. Then, write each word in the correct column according to its number of syllables.

1 syllable words	2 syllable words	3 syllable words
_____	_____	_____
_____	_____	_____
_____	_____	_____
_____	_____	_____
_____	_____	_____
_____	_____	_____
_____	_____	_____
_____	_____	_____
_____	_____	_____

Challenge:

_____ _____ _____

Word List
1. batter
2. figure
3. drive
4. round
5. reflect
6. anchor
7. pound
8. tense
9. minor
10. cooler
11. chest
12. capital
13. model
14. pants
15. counter
16. glasses
17. point
18. general
19. pupil
20. squash

Challenge Words
21. patient
22. measure

Practice B

Complete each sentence with one of these spelling words. You may use a dictionary to look up different meanings for each word.

anchor	tense	glasses	point	capital

1. Bernard washed the empty _____ .

2. Jerome's muscles felt _____ after work.

3. Start each sentence with a _____ letter.

4. The _____ is sharp so be careful.

5. They raised enough _____ to start a business.

6. Grandmother says it is rude to _____ at people.

7. Gloria threw the _____ over the side of the boat.

8. The present _____ of *knew* is *know.*

9. The news _____ talked about the stock market.

10. The hunters used field _____ , or binoculars.

Apply

Choose one of the challenge words and use it to write two sentences that illustrate different meanings of the homonym.

11. _____

12. _____

Name _____ Date _____

Sentence Combining with Appositives

Copyright © SRA/McGraw-Hill. Permission is granted to reproduce this page for classroom use.

Focus

An **appositive** is a noun that is placed next to another noun to identify it or add information about it.

Example: My brother, Jack, is four years old.

Jack is an appositive that describes *my brother.*

An **appositive phrase** is a group of words that includes an appositive and words that describe the appositive.

Example: Sara, Jecolia's mother, is very proud of her daughter.

Jecolia's mother is an appositive phrase that describes *Sara.*

- An appositive is usually set off by commas next to the noun it identifies.

- Appositives are *nouns.*

- Two sentences can be combined into one shorter sentence using appositives.

Example: I ate lunch with my friend. My friend is a fellow soccer player.

I ate lunch with my friend, a fellow soccer player.

Practice A

Read the following paragraph. Circle any appositives or appositive phrases you find. Underline the nouns they identify.

Tarah Rhodes, the Hollywood actress, is making an appearance in our small town today. She visited Ichabod, a neighboring town, yesterday. She has starred in over 20 movies. *Wandering,* her first movie, is one of my favorites. I hope to get her autograph and maybe a picture.

Practice B Appositives can make your writing more compact, make your sentences flow better, and add sentence variety. Change each of the following pairs of sentences into a single sentence, using an appositive or appositive phrase.

1. My brother is a wrestler. My brother loves to compete.

_____

2. I asked my mom how to do my math homework. My mom is a math whiz.

_____

_____

3. Sally's pet goat likes to chew on people's shoestrings. Sally's pet goat is

named Chomper. _____

_____

4. I walked to the park with Tommy. Tommy is my neighbor.

_____

5. Tug asked Mrs. Wills if Tanner could play. Mrs. Wills is Tanner's mom.

_____

Apply Write a sentence about each of the following people. Each sentence should contain an appositive or an appositive phrase.

6. basketball coach _____

_____

7. best friend _____

_____

Grammar, Usage, and Mechanics • *Skills Practice 2*

Name _____ **Date** _____

Superlative Adjectives and Adverbs

Focus | **Superlative adjectives and adverbs** compare three or more things.

- Superlative adjectives compare three or more *nouns.*

- Superlative adverbs compare three or more *verbs.*

Most superlatives end in *-est.*

- Adjective: Tran is the **tallest** girl in her family.

- Adverb: Beth swims the butterfly **fastest** of any of her teammates.

Sometimes we add *most* to form the superlatives. In these cases, **do not** add *-est.*

- Adjective: The puzzle was the **most challenging** one that Lisa had ever put together.

- Adverb: Sean is the one who can type the **most skillfully** in our group.

Some adjectives and adverbs have different superlative forms.

- Adjectives with different superlative forms include *good, bad,* and *many.*

- Her grandmother's soup is the **best** in town.

- Adverbs with different superlative forms include *well, badly, much,* and *little.*

- Of all the family members, Tia plays video games the **least.**

Practice A | **Read the sentences. Circle the correct superlative for each adjective.**

1. Which amusement park is (biggest/most big), Splash City, Waterfest, or World of Fun?

2. World of Fun has the (scariest/most scary) roller coaster that I've ever ridden.

Practice B

Read the sentences. Circle the correct superlative for each adverb.

3. Will was the person in our group waiting (patientest/most patiently) for his sandwich.

4. Will and Randy performed (best/most well) in the talent show.

5. Tara said she'd rather see which frog could jump (highest/most high) in the frog jumping contest.

Apply

Read the sentences. Write the superlative form of each word in parentheses in the blank at the end of each sentence.

6. Box turtles live the (long) of any animal on our planet. _____

7. The (important) thing to remember is your raincoat. _____

8. Today is the (bad) day Tina has had all week. _____

9. Sue cheered (loudly) of anyone in the crowd. _____

10. Jon's baseball collection is the (big) collection in town. _____

11. Leslie describes scenes the (well) out of anyone in our writing group.

_____

Name _____ Date _____

Selection Vocabulary

Focus

wealth (welth) *n.* A great amount of money. (page 606)

possessions (pə ze' shənz) Plural of the noun **possession:** A thing someone owns. (page 606)

protested (prə tes' təd) Past tense of the verb **protest:** To say in disagreement. (page 606)

fine (fīn) *adj.* Very nice. (page 606)

demanded (di man' dəd) Past tense of the verb **demand:** To ask firmly. (page 609)

discarded (dis kär' dəd) *adj.* Thrown away. (page 609)

Practice

Review the vocabulary words and definitions from "A Spoon for Every Bite." Write two sentences that each use at least one of the vocabulary words from this lesson.

1. _____

_____

2. _____

_____

_____

Apply   **Write the vocabulary word that fits each pair of examples.**

3. said you felt the rule was unfair; objected to shutting down the animal

shelter _____

4. buying a mansion and a yacht; living in luxury _____

5. put items out for the trash; threw things away you didn't need

_____

6. your mother told you to be kind to your sister; your father said not to cross

the busy street _____

7. your stuffed animal collection; your new computer _____

8. a large, sparkling diamond ring; a wedding gown _____

Name _____ **Date** _____

Compare and Contrast

Focus

Comparing and contrasting is one way to organize information in expository writing. It is sometimes useful to compare and contrast two items, such as two objects, two events, two ideas, or two people or characters. Comparing and contrasting details can help support the main idea in a piece of writing.

- When collecting or organizing information to compare and contrast, a Venn diagram is a good tool to use. Here's an example.

Cats and Dogs as Pets

Cats
- more independent
- don't need to be walked

Cats and Dogs
- fur needs grooming
- daily food and water

Dogs
- need a lot of attention
- need to be walked

Practice A

Create a Venn diagram to organize ideas for the following topic.

Compare and contrast two types of flowers or trees.

Practice B

Look at each pair of words below. Write how the items in each pair are different and how they are alike.

1. book   computer

Different: _____

_____

_____

Alike: _____

_____

2. babies   puppies

Different: _____

_____

_____

Alike: _____

_____

Now choose one of the word pairs and compare and contrast the items in one or two paragraphs. Remember to vary your sentence structure so your writing is interesting.

_____

_____

_____

_____

_____

Name _____ **Date** _____

Using the Card or Computer Catalog

The card or computer catalog lists all the books a library has. The catalog can be found in the library's computer or on cards in a file cabinet with small drawers. Look at the sample card below.

DICK WHITTINGTON

J

398.22   Storr, Catherine.

STO   Dick Whittington/retold by Catherine Storr;

illustrated by Jane Bottomly.—Milwaukee:

Raintree Children's Books, ©1986.

[32] p.: col. ill.; 25 cm.

Summary: Retells the traditional tale of the poor boy in medieval England who became Lord Mayor of London.

1. Whittington, Richard, d. 1423

2. Folklore—England.

Here is a list of information found on cards in a card catalog.

- There are three types of cards: **author, title,** and **subject** cards. Depending on the type of card, either the author's name, the title of the book, or the subject will be at the top of the card. For instance, the title appears at the top of a title card.

- The call number is in the upper left corner of every card. This number matches the numbers and letters on the spine of the book. This number tells you where to find the book in the library.

- Every card lists the year the book was published and the name and location of the publisher, the number of pages, the abbreviation *ill.* if the book has illustrations, and the size of the book.

- The card includes a brief summary of what the book is about.

- At the bottom of each card is a list that shows all the headings the book is listed under in the card catalog.

Find two books you might use for investigation. Record the information you find in the card catalog on the blank cards below. Make sure you copy the information as it appears on the cards.

Name _____ **Date** _____

Personal Letters via E-mail

Audience: Who is the audience for your character's personal e-mail?

_____

_____

Purpose: What is your character's reason for writing this e-mail?

_____

_____

Prewriting **Begin drafting the body of your personal e-mail, keeping in mind your character's audience and purpose. Answer the following questions as a review of how to write a personal e-mail message.**

1. What do you type after the word "To:"?

_____

_____

2. What is an example of a salutation?

_____

3. Where does the body of your e-mail start?

_____

4. What should you do before the beginning of each new paragraph?

_____

5. What are some words you could use for the closing of your e-mail?

_____

Revising — Use this checklist to revise your e-mail.

☐ Did I write everything I wanted to write?

☐ Are my tone and formality of language appropriate?

☐ Did I remember all the parts of an e-mail?

Editing/Proofreading — Use this checklist to correct mistakes in your e-mail. Use the delete and backspace keys to help you edit.

☐ Make sure that all words are spelled correctly.

☐ Check all punctuation to make sure that it is correct.

☐ Make sure sentences and proper nouns begin with capital letters.

Publishing — Use this checklist to get ready for publication.

☐ Click the word *Send* to send your e-mail.

☐ Print out a copy for yourself if you would like one.

Name _____ **Date** _____

Comparatives

Focus

• **Comparatives** are words that end in -er. They are adjectives that are used to compare two things

• Adding -er may require changes to the base word.
• Sometimes the y at the end of a base word changes to i before adding -er.

Practice A **Remove the suffix -er and write the base word for each spelling word.**

1. _____
2. _____
3. _____
4. _____
5. _____
6. _____
7. _____
8. _____
9. _____
10. _____
11. _____
12. _____
13. _____

14. _____
15. _____
16. _____
17. _____
18. _____
19. _____
20. _____

Challenge:

21. _____
22. _____

Word List

1. wealthier
2. finer
3. droopier
4. faster
5. larger
6. madder
7. wider
8. luckier
9. sleeker
10. surer
11. crabbier
12. slimmer
13. warmer
14. duller
15. lower
16. stiffer
17. littler
18. firmer
19. ruder
20. fresher

Challenge Words

21. healthier
22. tougher

Practice B

Write the spelling word that rhymes with each of the words below. Then, use the spelling word to write a sentence that compares two things.

1. sadder _____

_____

2. purer _____

_____

3. brittler _____

_____

4. flabbier _____

_____

5. grimmer _____

_____

Challenge

6. stealthier _____

_____

Apply

Write two spelling words that begin with the given letter. Choose words that would make sense in each sentence.

7. My dad's new car is s _____ than his old one.

_____ _____

8. These cherries are f _____ than the ones I bought last week.

_____ _____ _____

9. His old bike was l _____, so it fit under the porch.

_____ _____

Spelling • *Skills Practice 2*

Name _____ **Date** _____

Double Negatives

> **Focus** In English, we use only one negative word in a sentence. When two negatives occur in a sentence, we say the sentence contains a **double negative.** Some examples of negative words include *no, no one, nobody, none, not, nothing, nowhere,* and *never, aren't, won't, weren't, haven't,* and *isn't.*
>
> Example: She **doesn't** have **no** homework to do tonight.
>
> Corrected sentence: She **doesn't** have any homework to do tonight.

Practice A   **Read the sentences. Circle the double negatives, and rewrite the sentences correctly.**

1. Tyrone says there isn't no one who will help him finish painting the house.

_____

_____

2. Jake says he won't never help.

_____

3. Nobody in my family can come to none of my games this month.

_____

_____

4. I don't want no cookies that have coconut in them.

_____

_____

Practice B Each of the following sentences contains a double negative. On the line provided, write an affirmative word to replace the underlined word.

5. Kasey has never been to <u>no</u> baseball game. _____

6. Halley didn't do <u>nothing</u> wrong. _____

7. Pele never got <u>no</u> ice cream. _____

8. Grandma couldn't get <u>nowhere</u> because her car is being repaired.

_____

9. She <u>won't</u> tell me nothing about the soccer match. _____

10. She <u>hasn't</u> had no homework all week. _____

Apply Read the following sentences. Put an *X* in front of each sentence that contains a double negative.

11. _____ I hardly know nobody here.

12. _____ I can't remember the last time I saw her.

13. _____ No one told Bobby nothing about the game being cancelled.

14. _____ I couldn't have picked a better day for the garage sale.

15. _____ Mike can't eat none of that chocolate, or he'll get sick.

Name _____ Date _____

Contractions

Focus

A **contraction** is a shortened form of two words.

Examples:

does not = doesn't

can not = can't

will not = won't

should not = shouldn't

The contractions *they're, you're* and *it's* are the shortened forms of the words *they are, you are,* and *it is.* They are often confused with the possessive pronouns *their, your,* and *its. They're* is also sometimes mistaken for the word *there.*

Examples:

I know *they're* here somewhere.

Their favorite ice cream is vanilla.

What is in that big box over *there?*

Practice A

Replace the underlined words in each sentence with a contraction.

1. She <u>did not</u> tell me I was supposed to wear a suit. _____

2. I <u>would not</u> touch that stove if I were you. _____

3. I <u>can not</u> believe summer is here already. _____

4. <u>It is</u> great that you can help out today. _____

Practice B   **Read the sentences. Circle the correct word in parentheses.**

5. What time does (you're, your) brother's plane land?

6. His friends said (their, they're) going to pick him up at the airport at 2:00 P.M.

7. Since (its, it's) almost 1:30 P.M., they should leave soon.

8. Didn't you tell me that he's bringing his guitar and all of (it's, its) equipment with him?

9. (You're, Your) going to have a famous musician visiting you!

10. No, I'm not. (Its, It's) just my brother.

11. I'm going to watch the singers and (their, they're) workers get ready for the concert.

Apply   **Read the following sentences. If the underlined word is written incorrectly, write the correct word on the line. If the word is correct, write _Correct_ on the line.**

12. <u>Your</u> going to the fair tonight, right?   _____

13. I didn't get <u>they're</u> address before they left.   _____

14. Brett <u>doesnt</u> have a baseball cap to wear.   _____

15. Jake said he <u>won't</u> help move the equipment. _____

Name _____ **Date** _____

Selection Vocabulary

Focus

daydream (dā' drēm) *v.* To let the mind wander; to think about things that may not happen (page 623)

provide (prə vīd') *v.* To give something to someone (page 623)

value (val' yo͞o) *n.* Worth or importance (page 625)

worthless (wûrth' ləs) *adj.* Of no use or value (page 626)

miser (mī' zûr) *n.* A person who loves money more than anything else (page 627)

misfortune (mis' for' chən) *n.* Bad luck (page 627)

Practice

Write the vocabulary word that best matches the underlined word or phrase in the sentences below.

1. I often <u>let my mind wander</u> when I'm supposed to be doing

   homework. _____

2. I feel sorry for Rachel, who has had a lot of <u>bad luck</u>

   lately. _____

3. My grandpa's neighbor is a grumpy <u>person who loves money more than</u>

   <u>anything else</u>. _____

4. This hose has a tear in it and is practically

   <u>of no use.</u> _____

5. Your teacher will <u>give you</u> everything you need for

   the test. _____

6. The photo album might not be worth money, but it is of great <u>importance</u>

   to me. _____

Apply   **Write the word that best fits each clue below.**

1. Bad things have happened to you all day long. What do we call this?

_____

2. You give blankets and bottled water to people who have survived a hurricane.

What do you do for them? _____

3. You love money even more than you love people. What are you?

_____

4. Your mind wanders a lot. You imagine things that might happen someday.

What do you do? _____

5. Your grandpa's antique lamp is worth a lot of money. What does it have?

_____

6. Your bike tire has been punctured and can't be repaired. What is it?

_____

Vocabulary • *Skills Practice 2*

Name _____ Date _____

Gathering Information

Before you begin to gather information, decide on a topic to research for your investigation.

- My group's topic:

  _____

  _____

- Information I need to find or figure out about my topic:

  _____

  _____

  _____

  _____

Complete the chart below to help you decide which sources will be useful.

Sources	Useful?	How?
Encyclopedias		
Books		
Magazines		
Newspapers		
Videotapes, filmstrips, etc.		

Drawing Conclusions from Information

Drawing conclusions from the information you find for your investigation will help you learn as you read and write. You draw conclusions by carefully reading the details and facts in the material you are reading. The conclusion may not be stated but should be supported by examples from the text.

Read the information below about sea mammals.

Whales, dolphins, manatees, seals, sea lions, and sea otters are marine mammals. Marine mammals spend most of their time underwater, but must come to the surface to breathe. Whales were once hunted for their blubber, oil, and bones. Seals and sea otters were hunted for their fur. Today, most nations have laws protecting marine mammals.

• What conclusions about marine mammals can you make after reading the paragraph? Use the information above to draw conclusions about sea mammals.

_____

_____

_____

_____

_____

_____

_____

_____

_____

Name _____ **Date** _____

Pattern Poem

Audience: Who is the audience for your pattern poem?

_____

Purpose: What is your reason for writing a pattern poem?

_____

_____

Prewriting **Use this graphic organizer to plan your poem. Use a character or idea from one of the stories from this unit as your topic. Place your topic in the center circle. In each box, write descriptions or ideas that fit your topic.**

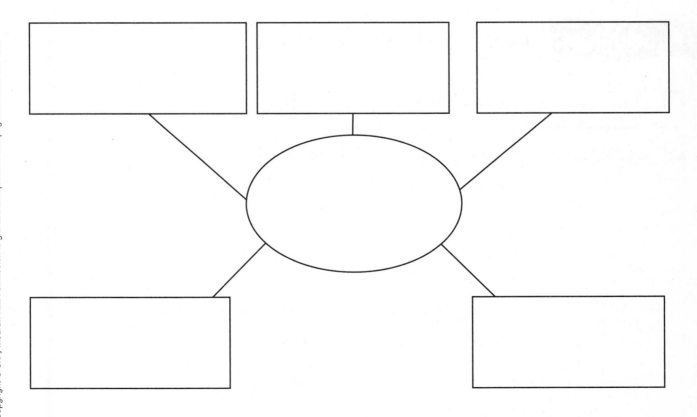

Revising   Use this checklist to revise your pattern poem.

☐ Do you create vivid images for your readers?

☐ Did you use rhyme and repetition?

☐ Do your phrases fit together and flow well?

☐ Is your pattern enjoyable to listen to?

Editing/Proofreading   Use this checklist to correct mistakes in your pattern poem.

☐ Are all words spelled correctly?

☐ Is all punctuation within your poem correct and consistent?

☐ Read your poem aloud to catch errors in rhythm and rhyme.

Publishing   Use this checklist to get ready for publication.

☐ Print out or write a neat final copy. Center the poem on the paper.

☐ Organize a poetry reading with your classmates.

Name _____ **Date** _____

Superlatives

Focus

- **Superlatives** are words that end in -*est*.
- They are adjectives that are used to compare more than two things.
- Adding -*est* may require changes to the base word. Sometimes the *y* at the end of a base word changes to *i* before adding -*est*.

Practice A **Remove the suffix -*est* and write the base word for each spelling word.**

1. _____
2. _____
3. _____
4. _____
5. _____
6. _____
7. _____
8. _____
9. _____
10. _____
11. _____
12. _____
13. _____
14. _____
15. _____
16. _____
17. _____
18. _____
19. _____
20. _____

Challenge:

21. _____
22. _____
23. _____

Word List

1. strictest
2. wildest
3. flattest
4. greatest
5. sleepiest
6. hugest
7. cleverest
8. slowest
9. sickest
10. saddest
11. cruelest
12. kindest
13. cleanest
14. loveliest
15. wisest
16. steepest
17. trimmest
18. hungriest
19. fairest
20. rarest

Challenge Words

21. messiest
22. vaguest
23. sassiest

Practice B

Choose the best word to use in each sentence. Write the word on the line.

1. My big brother is the (hungry, hungrier, hungriest) person I know.

_____

2. It was the (sad, sadder, saddest) movie I've ever seen.

_____

3. The (sick, sicker, sickest) patients are seen first.

_____

4. The crow is (clever, cleverer, cleverest) than the spider.

_____

5. Miss Palmer is a very (fair, fairer, fairest) teacher.

_____

Challenge

6. Paint is (messy, messier, messiest) than chalk.

_____

Apply

Circle the words that are spelled correctly.

7. cleanest   cleenest   clennest

8. greatist   gratest   greatest

9. loveliest   lovliest   lovelyest

10. steapest   steepest   steppest

Name _____ Date _____

Participial Phrases

> **Focus**
> - A **participle** is a verb form used as an adjective. Add *-ing* to a verb to form the present participle, and add *-ed* to a verb to form the past participle, unless the verb is irregular.
> - A **phrase** is a group of words used as a single part of speech. It may contain a verb, but it does not contain the verb's subject.
> - A **participial phrase** is a group of words that begins with a participle and modifies a noun or pronoun.
>
> Example: **Spinning in a circle,** LaRae lost her balance.
>
> **Participial phrases** can be used to combine two sentences, making your writing flow more smoothly.
>
> Example: Flo looked at her new bike. At the same time, she was grinning.
>
> New sentence: Grinning, Flo looked at her new bike.

Practice A Read the following sentences and underline the participial phrase in each.

1. Cluttered with magazines and newspapers, the table was not a very clean place to work.

2. Looking at us carefully, Claire said, "Are you sure you want to sit here?"

3. Reaching for her chair, she sat down slowly.

Practice B   Combine the pairs of sentences into a single sentence using a participial phrase. Write the new sentence on the line provided.

4. The baseball player was limping badly. He made it safely to first base.

_____

_____

5. My mom was filled with happiness. She welcomed my brother home from his trip.

_____

_____

6. Our house is located in front of a forest. Our house has a nice view from our back window.

_____

_____

Apply   For each noun, write a sentence with a participial phrase that describes it.

7. **elephant**

_____

8. **student**

_____

_____

9. **cheerleader**

_____

Name _____ Date _____

Comparative Adjectives and Adverbs

Focus

Comparative adjectives and adverbs compare two things.

• Comparative adjectives compare two *nouns.*

• Comparative adverbs compare two *verbs.*

Most comparatives end in *-er.*

• Adjective: Tran is **taller** than her older sister.

• Adverb: Beth swims the butterfly **faster** than her teammates.

Sometimes we add *more* to form comparatives. In these cases, **do not** add *-er.*

• Adjective: The puzzle was **more challenging** than the one Lisa received for her birthday.

• Adverb: Sean can type **more skillfully** than the other members of our group.

Some adjectives and adverbs have different comparative forms.

• Adjectives with different comparative forms include *good, bad,* and *many.*

  • Her grandmother's soup is **better** than the soup at the Main Street Diner.

• Adverbs with different comparative forms include *well, badly, much,* and *little.*

  • Tia plays video games **less** than her brother does.

Practice A

Read the sentences. Circle the correct comparative for each adjective.

1. My new puppy is (smaller/more small) than my other dog.

2. The corner deli has (better/gooder) sandwiches than the store across the street.

3. Our day at the park was (funner/more fun) than I thought it would be.

Practice B

Read the sentences. Circle the correct comparative for each adverb.

4. Candace is (carefuller/more careful) with her glass animals than with any other thing she owns.

5. I write fantasy scenes (badder/worse) than any of my friends.

6. Tom spoke (quieter/more quietly) in the library than he did in the hall.

Apply

Read the sentences. Write the comparative form of each word in parentheses in the blank at the end of each sentence.

7. It is (important) to brush your teeth than to watch TV. _____

_____

8. This cartoon is (funny) than the other one. _____

9. I can throw a ball (high) than my brother can. _____

10. Mom's suitcase is (big) than mine. _____

11. Sarah has (little) homework tonight than she did last night.

_____

12. Polar bears can swim (easily) in cold water than humans can.

_____

Word Structure • *Skills Practice 2*

Name _____ Date _____

Selection Vocabulary

Focus

opposing (ə pō' zing) *adj.* On the other side of an issue (page 637)

investment (in vest' mənt) *n.* Money someone puts into a business in order to make more money (page 637)

stencils (sten' səlz) *n.* Plural of **stencil:** a cut-out pattern used for making letter shapes with paint or markers (page 638)

partner (pärt' nûr) *n.* Someone who owns a business with another person (page 638)

profits (pro' fəts) *n.* Plural of **profit:** money a business earns (page 639)

century (sent' shə rē) *n.* A span of one hundred years (page 640)

corny (kor' nē) *adj.* Old-fashioned or sappy (page 643)

product (pro' dukt) *n.* Item that is sold by a business (page 646)

Practice Fill in each blank with a vocabulary word from this lesson to complete each sentence.

1. My mom is a _____ in the law firm.

2. Gracie made a risky _____, but if it works out, she'll have a lot of money.

3. Kylene used _____ to paint her name on her bedroom wall.

4. Our _____ is selling well, because it's something everyone can use.

5. Javier's great-grandfather has been alive for almost a _____.

6. I know my ideas are often _____, but this one is really good.

Apply **Write the word from the word box that matches each definition below.**

7. _____ money someone puts into a business in order to make more money

8. _____ money a business earns

9. _____ item that is sold by a business

10. _____ on the other side of an issue

11. _____ cut-out patterns used for making letter shapes with paint or markers

12. _____ one hundred years

13. _____ old-fashioned or sappy

14. _____ someone who goes into business with others

Name _____ **Date** _____

Primary and Secondary Sources

Primary sources such as diaries, journals, or newspapers are useful resources for investigation. Secondary sources, or resources that offer background information on a primary source, also aid a researcher in the investigation process. In the boxes below, record examples of primary and secondary sources you have used in your investigation.

Title: _____ Author: _____

Type of primary source: _____

What did you learn from this resource? _____

_____

_____

Title: _____ Author: _____

Type of primary source: _____

What did you learn from this resource? _____

_____

_____

Title: _____ Author: _____

Type of secondary source: _____

What did you learn from this resource? _____

_____

Title: _____ Author: _____

Type of secondary source: _____

What did you learn from this resource? _____

_____

Title: _____ Author: _____

Type of secondary source: _____

What did you learn from this resource? _____

_____

Name _____ **Date** _____

Diamante Poem

Think

Audience: Who is the audience for your diamante poem?

_____

Purpose: What is your reason for writing a diamante poem?

_____

Prewriting

Use this graphic organizer to plan your poem. Write the topic of your poem at the top of the chart. Then fill in nouns, participles, and adjectives that you can use in your diamante.

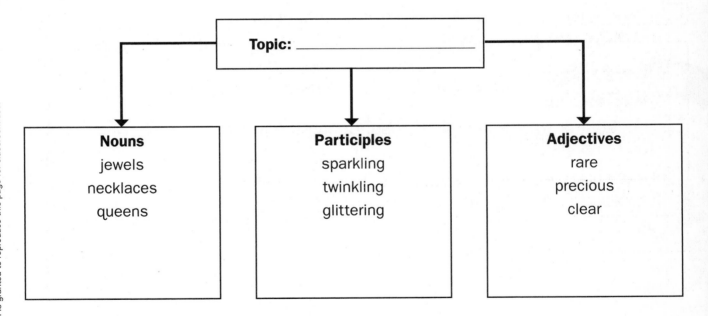

Topic: _____

Nouns	Participles	Adjectives
jewels	sparkling	rare
necklaces	twinkling	precious
queens	glittering	clear

Revising   Use this checklist to revise your diamante poem.

- ☐ Did the words you chose add meaning to the poem?
- ☐ Did you use alliteration and assonance?
- ☐ Did you use several different kinds of imagery to add interest?
- ☐ Do your words evoke emotion?

Editing/Proofreading   Use this checklist to correct mistakes in your diamante poem.

- ☐ Are all words spelled correctly?
- ☐ Did you use the correct parts of speech?
- ☐ Read your poem aloud to detect parts that need improvement.

Publishing   Use this checklist to get ready for publication.

- ☐ Print out or write a neat final copy. Center the poem on the paper.
- ☐ Have your teacher display all the diamante poems on a wall or bulletin board.

Name _____ Date _____

Free Verse

Think

Audience: Who is the audience for your free verse poem?

_____

Purpose: What is your reason for writing a free verse poem?

_____

_____

Prewriting

Use this graphic organizer to plan your poem. Choose an image to use as your topic. Write that topic in the center circle. Write thoughts and ideas about your topic on the lines.

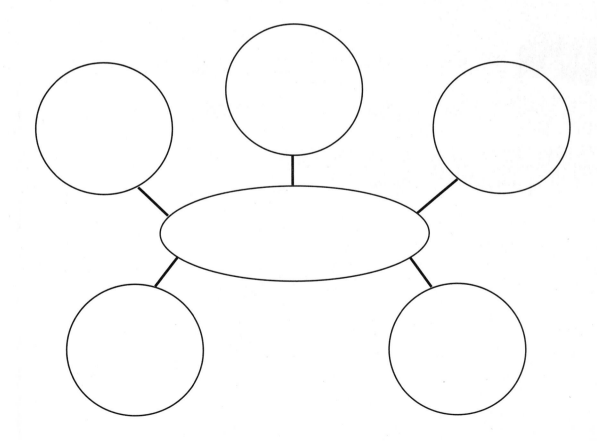

Revising   Use this checklist to revise your free-verse poem.

☐ Did the words you chose add meaning to the poem?

☐ Did you use onomatopoeic words or figurative language?

☐ Did you use several different kinds of imagery to add detail and interest?

Editing/Proofreading   Use this checklist to correct mistakes in your free-verse poem.

☐ Are all words spelled correctly?

☐ Did you use the correct punctuation?

☐ Read your poem aloud to detect parts that need improvement.

Publishing   Use this checklist to get ready for publication.

☐ Print out or write a neat final copy. Center the poem on the paper.

☐ Read your poem to the class, being sure to concentrate on diction and clarity.

Name _____ **Date** _____

Contractions

Focus

- **Contractions are shortened forms of two or more words.**
- Contractions are made by leaving out at least one letter and using an apostrophe instead.
- Some contractions are **homophones,** meaning they sound alike but are spelled differently.

Practice A Write the contraction for each pair of words

1. what is _____

2. could not _____

3. when is _____

4. it will _____

5. here is _____

6. I have _____

7. you are _____

8. did not _____

9. I had _____

10. let us _____

11. she would _____

Challenge

12. should have _____

Word List

1. I've
2. wouldn't
3. he's
4. you've
5. you're
6. hadn't
7. when's
8. I'd
9. couldn't
10. here's
11. didn't
12. where's
13. you'll
14. she'd
15. who's
16. they've
17. let's
18. he'd
19. it'll
20. what's

Challenge Words

21. should've
22. who'll

Practice B

Some contractions are homonyms. Test each sentence below by saying the words for each contraction. Then, write the word that makes the sentence correct.

13. Jenni (here's, hears) the television downstairs.

_____

14. I suppose (he'd, heed) rather have the new one.

_____

15. (Who's, Whose) washing the dishes tonight?

_____

16. Where is (you're, your) coat?

_____

Apply

Write out the words that each of these contractions stand for.

17. they've   _____

18. who's   _____

19. where's   _____

20. he'd   _____

Challenge

21. should've   _____

22. who'll   _____

Name _____ Date _____

Verb Tenses

Focus **Verb tenses** show when an action takes place in a sentence.

- A **present tense** verb shows the action is happening now. To form the present tense, add -*s* or -*es* to a regular verb that has a singular subject in a sentence. If the subject is plural, do not add -*s* or -*es* to the verb.
  Example: The horse **jumps.** The horses **jump.**

- A **past tense** verb tells about action that has already taken place. To form the past tense of a regular verb with a singular or plural subject, add -*ed* to the verb.
  Example: The horse **jumped.** The horses **jumped.**

- Some verbs don't follow rules for forming the past tense. **Irregular verbs** change their spelling for the past tense.
  Example: The jockey **rides** the horse. (present tense) The jockey **rode** the horse. (past tense)

- The **future tense** tells about an action that will happen in the future. Use the helping verb *will* in front of the base form of a verb to show the future tense.
  Example: The horse **will jump** over the water.

Practice **Read this paragraph. Change the underlined verbs from the present tense to the past tense. Write the correct word above the incorrrect one.**

Alexander Fleming <u>live</u> from 1881 to 1955. He <u>discover</u> penicillin. In a lab

experiment, Dr. Fleming <u>have</u> bacteria growing in a container. Some mold <u>get</u> into

the experiment by accident and <u>kill</u> the bacteria. This discovery <u>help</u> create a

brand-new medicine.

Practice B

Read the sentences. Change the words in parentheses to either the past tense or the future tense. Write the correct word above the word in parentheses.

1. Jorge (study) tomorrow for the science test.

2. Questions about seven famous scientists (be) on tomorrow's exam.

3. Damon and Duane (study) yesterday afternoon.

4. Later that evening, their mother (tell) them to go upstairs to wash up for supper.

5. Yesterday, Jorge (call) Damon and Duane to ask them some questions about the test.

6. After Jorge called, the two brothers (decide) to help Jorge.

7. All three boys think they (do) well on the test tomorrrow.

Apply

Read this paragraph. Change the underlined verbs to either the past tense or the future tense. Use proofreading marks to show changes. Write the correct word over the incorrect word.

Alexandra <u>is</u> sick yesterday. She <u>take</u> the science test tomorrow. The rest of the class <u>take</u> it two days ago. When I go to science class today, Mr. Crawford <u>tell</u> us when he <u>give</u> us our tests back. I hope that it <u>be</u> soon. The test <u>is</u> not that difficult for me, but I <u>study</u> for it for two hours. I wonder how the other kids <u>do</u>?

Grammar, Usage, and Mechanics • *Skills Practice 2*